Homebuilt
Firearms

by

Gary F. Hartman

Published by
Gary F. Hartman
Lebanon, OR

Homebuilt
Firearms

———————————————

Copyright © 2010
by Gary F. Hartman

ISBN 978-0-9815399-2-8
Library of Congress
Control Number: 2010908062

Printed in U.S.A. By Lightning Source Inc.

Acknowledgment

I wish to thank my wife, Janie, and some very close friends, former work buddies from China Lake, California.... Sidney Busch, Jerry Allen, Joe Munk and Hank Eberhart for their encouragement in my writing and building of the guns for this book.

I often had the dinner table covered in parts and pieces and tracked in metal dust from grinding and welding in the garage. And on some occasions, my wife came home to find the garage cluttered with my project material, and had to come into the house through the rain. I think she only whacked me on the head a couple times with her umbrella!

Thankfully in doing the book well prior to the holiday season, I did not have to remove and put away the parts to clean the house for company and visitors. Thus I was spared an unfortunate way to demonstrate Murphy's Law, losing and misplacing critical items for the project.

Amazon.com was an excellent source for springs and small parts. A local metal fabrication shop here in Lebanon helped with cutting of heavy steel.

Various Government agencies such as the Copyright office and Library of Congress were very helpful in the setup of the book. And Lightning Source and Ingram are outstanding printer and wholesale book agencies. Working with them has always been a positive experience.

Gary F. Hartman
Lebanon, OR
www.jgenasplace.com

Table of
Contents

Chapter 1

Basic Considerations,
Why Guns?

Our Heritage

A firearm has always been the prime implement of self defense and safety, and the use of guns is a historical part of our entire American heritage.

When the Continental Army first formed and General George Washington took command outside Boston, all manner of men appeared to fight for freedom and our country, they varied in age from teenage boys to old men in their 80's... and each brought their own personal firearm.

If you get a chance, read David McCullough's **"1776"** to get an idea of the courage and toughness of these citizen soldiers.

The meaning of the Second Amendment as developed years later essentially refers to the fact that a Militia being necessary to protect against any despotic government leads to an obvious fact that the right to keep and bear arms is an individual right. Those men who made up the militia were *expected* to provide their own firearms, a firearm was a recognized tool of every pioneer citizen.

This individual right is a basic right inherent from birth, the right to life and self defense. It does not matter really if a document defines that right.

From the time I was young, like most any kid, I was interested in guns. First as a small boy riding a broom and playing cowboys and Indians, eventually in my teens going out into the woods of Oregon, California, Nevada and Montana, there always was the possibility of a dangerous animal encounter, and of course a kid's imagination is always conjuring up something.

In The Dalles, Oregon in the 50's I saw two Cougars from a distance on two occasions, once near Chenowith School near the West end of town, and once near Petersburg School S.E. of town.

In Trout Creek, Montana a couple years later, my brother and sister saw a Black Bear out in the woods rooting in a stump and ran home in a fright. An animal encounter was obviously a possibility.

Eventually in 10th grade in Verdi, Nevada, I received a Stevens tubular feed semi-auto .22 rifle for Christmas or a birthday. Suddenly in going out into the woods, I had a real means of defense against any danger. From that point on I was a charter member of that historic group of rugged independent woodsmen of old, feeling confident and safe out in the wilderness, alone except for my rifle!

Nowadays, Cougar sighting are becoming more and more common. Not to mention assaults and other criminal activity, both in urban and outdoor environments. A firearm was always and still is to this day a considerable and reliable means of defense, self reliance and survival.

Even a .22 caliber rifle as described in this book is an excellent varmint weapon, and is useful for hunting small game. It is also a significant means of defense in a home which lacks a more powerful weapon.

Chapter 2

Safety Considerations
and Tools

My purpose in writing this book is to show an approach to a new multi-round firearm design, an idea I had thought long and hard about while attending the Authors' Table at the Oregon State Fair in 2009. It got me thinking, *I could build this firearm. A person could build a firearm with garage tools!*

With this book I set out to do it, describing the making of firearms, in actual fact, *my making a firearm. No lathe or Milling Machine, just garage tools. The gun is rough, but functional.*

A prime consideration is safety. Even the metal working involved requires care and concentration towards preventing an accident. The described firearm fabrication requires a great deal of care and accuracy in measurements, cartridges must align perfectly with the barrel on firing, metal thickness must be sufficient for safety.

Any time a person works with metal, he will encounter sharp edges, edges that need to be filed to remove a jagged edge or knife sharp burr. So I had to be very cautious!

This book is not intended to guide you into making a firearm unless you are totally dedicated to do it, it is more an explanation of my efforts to do a fabrication of my own. At most it is an illustration that a hobbyist who is careful and diligent can perhaps build a working firearm himself.

If you should decide to undertake such a project yourself, the effort falls upon *your* responsibility in the entire picking of materials, construction, everything; you assume all risk and liability for your own construction as well as function of your own firearm.

I cannot examine metals used by others, I cannot be responsible for another person's workmanship or the care they apply towards using powerful tools in making a dangerous device anymore than I am responsible for their driving a car. Those are all things I have no influence over.

However, I believe a hobbyist or person with reasonable mechanical ability and considerable patience can achieve and complete such a project.

Many tools are required, at the least, a Bench Vise, a Drill Press, Bench Grinder, and Angle Grinder, files, a Hacksaw, a Wire Welder and Dremel type tool, center punch, drill bits, Vise Grip Pliers, etc.. An ability to weld is also necessary.

The Angle Grinder can use cutoff blades to allow cutting and shaping of many of the steel parts.

Grinding with either the Bench Grinder or the Angle Grinder causes hot particles, a fire hazard if you let the sparks fly near any combustibles. Grinding above a floor with combustible solvents, Gasoline, etc. is a route to disaster! Never allow your body or face to align with the spinning disk!

Eye and ear protection are needed. Welding also has hot beads of material being expelled as you weld. And work which remains hot for some time!

The Dremel type miniature tools have cutting disks available that allow precision small cutting and grinding of metal. They came in very handy for precision parts in the gun.

4

A necessary piece to accompany the Drill Press is an adjustable machine vise. Some of these have two axis adjustment for very accurate drilling. A person would need this item for accurate drilling.

A good general rule for all work on this type of project is: Wear Safety Glasses at all times! Be cautious of hot pieces, sparks flying into combustibles, think every work process through beforehand and make sure your area is safe.

These are dangerous and powerful tools, and a builder should become familiar with the proper use and safe operation of each. He should always wear appropriate safety goggles or better still, a **full face shield**, also dust masks and hearing protection while using them. The premise is to follow the instructions provided with each tool.

The hobbyist-builder is the sole person responsible for the tasks involved and the final result. The designs shown herein are a logical result of my endeavors, **but that doesn't mean they are risk free.**

So if you wish to attempt a similar project, you must use caution, follow procedures as described in the tool manuals, and use your head.

It is very difficult to fabricate and weld every single metal item in the construction perfectly, there will be times when the builder is dissatisfied and will redo a particular step. That is part of life, Murphy's Law, just the way it goes sometimes.

A good suggestion for a Wire Welder: when finished wire welding, a person should always loosen the wire feed drive wheel spring inside the welder so it won't weaken...and readjust the next time he welds.

If I did some work on a piece and was then going to weld it into place, I always tried to cover the already machined portions with a piece of scrap metal to protect from weld spatter. Splatter beads can usually be scraped off, or filed, but if a person eliminates them getting on the surfaces at the beginning, all the

5

better.

When fillet welding a vertical piece to a flat piece, I tried to tilt the vertical piece a bit away from the side I was welding on- perhaps 3 degrees, ... the weld will "pull" as it cools and the piece will be crooked without the prior tilting. Practice to get the feel for this.

An important criterion: A person should avoid a future explosion of a weapon project due to poor workmanship or faulty alignment; that means doing careful work, checking the critical measurements, being careful of not cutting corners.

Once the firearm is built, there should be a long test interval to observe that operation is as desired and no impending failures are imminent.

I used a good deal of time testing with a rigged test firing pallet; a good idea for a couple hundred rounds, examining the weapon, cartridge bar block and barrel after every few rounds to check for deformation, cracking, fouling or signs of a problem.

If you should choose to try such a project as I did; remember, *it is your gun, and your workmanship, and you are totally responsible for properly constructing it, for choosing the correct materials, testing it to assure it is safe and for using it with regard to others' and your safety.*

Drilling in Steel

In drilling many holes in steel on the drill press, there are several important things to remember when doing so:

- Safety
- lubrication
- Speed
- pressure

A person should NEVER wear a long sleeve shirt or something that could entangle in the spinning tool or catch a hand. He should **Wear safety goggles** To Be SAFE!

No matter what, a person is drilling in steel; using oil or a cutting fluid to lubricate and cool the bit is the proper technique. Engine oil can be used, whatever is used in an auto, the builder can put some into a small shop oil can. He can put a squirt on the surface or tip of the bit prior to drilling and at intervals while drilling, raise the bit and apply a couple drops into the hole as he goes. It is a good idea to stop the Drill Press occasionally and wipe the work and clean up the drill material, keeping a fairly clean work area.

The rule is to use a High Speed Steel Drill Bit, wood drilling bits are not capable of drilling in steel.
When drilling with smaller bits, say 3/32 to 1/8 a person should use the higher speed settings or pulleys of the Drill Press.

On larger bits like the #1 drill bit, I used a lower speed setting. A hobbyist builder can grab a metal working book at the library to assist, but if experienced, he can also estimate fairly closely- if he has only a simple 5 speed drill press as I do... I used the mid to fastest speed for the 3/32 bit; and the slowest speed for the #1 bit.

On applying drilling pressure, the builder can rapidly get to a comfortable confidence here:

I believe I applied 2 to 4 lbs on the drill press lever, the drill then cut evenly and easily at some point, I was amazed at how easily the bit cut steel.

A builder must not apply more force once he finds the point where the bit cuts nicely. Going too slow can allow the steel to harden; going too fast can damage the bit or stall the drill press. He must always use plenty of oil at short intervals, perhaps each 3/16 or 1/4" or so of penetration, it is a good idea to raise the bit and apply a squirt of oil to the hole, then reapply the bit to the work. If the drilling is done too fast or without oil, the work can overheat and harden or damage the drill bit.

As a hobbyist-builder gains experience and confidence he will move smoothly through the drilling process.

If you take this project on, always try to work carefully and work SAFELY!

Wood Parts

The stock construction will require some woodworking tools and abilities: A Table Saw, Jigsaw or Sabre Saw, and sanders. You will need clamps to glue the laminations together. Safety is the first priority here as well... Safety Glasses, Ear Protectors and a Dust Mask.
****

So, if you wish to continue on such a project, this is essentially a description of my efforts and a guide to my route of construction, a rough series of ideas that eventually resulted in the firearms described..

If you take a similar route, it is at your own risk, the entire responsibility must be your own!
A basic rule for anyone attempting such a project: **Don't cut corners on safety!**

Chapter 3

Description of
The Basic Firearm

Most people are familiar with revolvers to some extent, they are a weapon that has been around for a long time and they are reliable and fairly simple in operation.

They consist of a frame which houses the operating mechanism to operate a hammer and positioning mechanism for a rotating cylinder.

The cylinder has several radial chambers to hold the cartridges, usually five to nine in number. A barrel is attached to the frame and the cocking-hammer and cylinder mechanism is designed to cause each increment of the cylinder rotation to accurately align a cartridge chamber with the barrel. At this point, the cylinder locks in place.

Two types of mechanism actions are common, *single action* and *double action.*

Single action means the hammer must be manually cocked, simultaneously aligning and locking the cylinder chamber with the barrel. Then the trigger is pulled only to release the cocked hammer and fire the cartridge.

Double action is designed to operate from trigger action .. as the trigger is pulled, it first rotates and locks the cylinder chamber in alignment with the barrel; it locks the position just before the final movement of the trigger releases the hammer to fall and fire the cartridge.

A New Design

The firearm described in this book use a similar action, but there is no round cylinder... instead the housing for the cartridges is a solid rectangular steel bar with individual chambers for each cartridge, a "Linear Bar Magazine", which replaces the cylinder. It resembles a "clip" like those used in a semi-auto pistol or repeater or semi-auto rifle but the cartridges remain in place in each chamber, they do not feed nor eject as in a conventional clip feed magazine. Instead, as each round is fired, the entire bar ratchets to the next chamber-barrel alignment, the next cartridge fires and the bar unit eventually falls from the weapon when all cartridges are expended. A new "Linear Magazine" can then be inserted to allow another sequence of several rounds. This action is similar to a clip fed weapon.

The spacing of the respective individual chambers is essentially determined by the particular used gun barrel you obtain as its diameter determines the minimum position of a ball detent, which is the lock for each firing position of the bar magazine.

Advantages

I envisioned some important advantages to this method: in any semi-auto or repeating firearm, jams always occur on chambering or ejection of a cartridge or casing. This bar type magazine with the cartridges and expended casings remaining in place inherits no such fault, and hopefully will eliminate jams. Simply actuating the hammer or pulling the trigger is intended to move a new round into place without a jam. *If some blow dislodges the alignment of the bar magazine, the next cocking actuation will advance to the next round without a jam.*

Also a mechanical action similar to a simple revolver type action can be used rather than a complicated ejection/feed type mechanism as is required for conventional magazine fed weapons.

Disadvantages

The main disadvantage to this design is the bar forms the actual chamber for each round, it does not have the large capacity of a high capacity type magazine, typically eight to ten rounds may be a usable figure. Also, the magazine is heavy, **especially if it lands on your foot!**

Initially I expected to be using a .22 L.R. caliber design, and figured the bar magazine could hold 8 to 10 rounds certainly in the smaller caliber.

A second irregularity is since the bar magazine must increment on each shot, it moves *through* the weapon, and to avoid interaction with sighting, it makes sense to move downward as it proceeds.

However, that design dictates the barrel must be at the bottom front of the frame (receiver) .

But the design could also have the barrel at the top conventionally and place the sights on the side of the rifle.. *similar to the British Bren with its top magazine* - in fact when you think about it, in normal rifle sighting you must twist your neck and head over the top of a conventional rifle in order to sight. It likely is much more natural to sight *alongside* the rifle as would be done if the magazine bar exits the top!

So you have various choices here. Bottom exit... or top exit; also by utilizing a raised front sight on the bottom exit configuration similar to an AR-15 rifle or an AK-47, this sighting situation can be easily accommodated. (Or on the top exit design, a side sight respectively.) Or use a side sight anyway… because you won't have to tweak your neck! However, with a side sight the rifle becomes right or left handed, another thing to remember. You see the trade-offs.

The homemade firearms described in this book will be made using scrap steel as available from metal fabricators... except for the barrel, which you will purchase used from a gun show.

You can probably find a common 20 inch barrel used, very typical from older .22 rifles, Stevens, Western Field, J.C. Higgins, Remington, Mossberg, etc. Sometimes some portion of the receiver or chamber will be a part of the assembly, this is good. A portion of the hardened steel may be very usable for the firing pin portion of the hammer you fabricate!

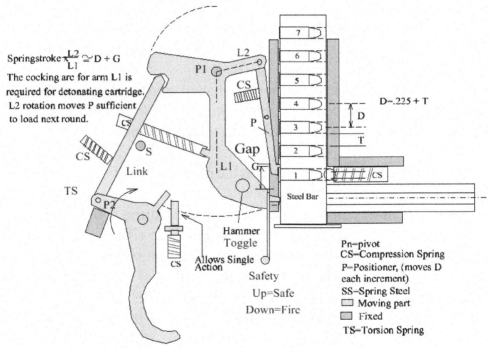

Fig. 1. Basic Assembly

At a metal fabricator ask if you may get some material from their scrap bin: obtain a strip of steel of 1/4" thickness, 2" wide and approx. 12 inches long, some 3/16" steel in similar width, also some 2" wide strips of sheet steel approximately 12 ga. thick. For the receiver portion you will need 14 ga. steel, approx 4 inches wide and perhaps 30 inches long. And of course a 4 ½ inch wide by ½ inch thick Steel bar from which you can cut several bar magazines.

You can have some cutting work done at a local welder/ fabricator shop if it is difficult. The bar magazine will be 1/2" or thicker steel, it might be very handy to have a shop cut this heavy piece to size.

If you have the thick pieces cut in a shop, inspect and file any cutting waste nibs off the corner of the cut magazine bar pieces. The other thinner parts can probably be cut or shaped with the Hacksaw, Angle Grinder, a Bench Grinder and a file. Small details or slots can be cut with a Dremel type tool and cutting disks. Once you determine the slot dimensions, you can drill a multiple series of holes, then use the Dremel tool with cutter disk to cut out between, finally filing to finish the slot.

This book describes a lower exit magazine bar weapon. See a simplified representative diagram of a possible firearm action in Figure 1. A bolt firing pin mechanism could also be used instead of a hammer. I chose the hammer for less friction.

I found that drilling the bar magazine left slight ridges in the holes and upon firing real rounds, the casings expanded enough to require driving them out, they would not simply fall out. If you make four or five magazines, you could always drive the casings out on returning home after shooting, or bring a small punch and hammer to do so in the field.

Of course being homemade this is a minor irritation, but if you need to, you can have the holes reamed at a gunsmith.

Chapter 4

General Details,
Materials,
and
The Bar Magazine

The single action repeater uses a far simpler mechanism than the double action weapon described later. The cocking is done manually, it also positions the cartridge in alignment with the barrel; then the bolt/hammer catching device locks it in the cocked position.
Pulling the trigger only releases the bolt/hammer assembly.

Steel Bar Magazine
Considerations

In either this weapon or the later double action weapon, the steel bar magazine is a very critical part, so it can be constructed first. I used a steel bar ½ inch thick. With this thickness it seems to be a good approach to have this piece cut at a machine or metal fabrication shop.

A .22 long rifle cartridge is approximately .225 inch in diameter and one inch in length. So the bar must be approximately 1.25

inches wide, leaving a quarter inch gap between the bullet and the barrel opening, this is also plenty to allow a ball detent positioning device for locking chamber to barrel alignment.

There is an engineering purpose here, the space needs to be sufficient to allow the detent, but yet not too large to add unnecessary magazine bar weight or so large a space to allow large pressure loss before the bullet enters the barrel.

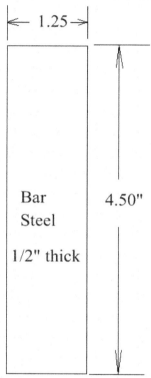

Fig. 2. Bar Magazine

A .22 L.R. cartridge develops a high pressure on detonation. According to tables, it could be 24,000 p.s.i. A very high value!

Mild steel has two values of stress capability, one is tensile strength, the other is shear. Tensile strength is pull-apart strength perpendicular to a cross section area of surface, shear is a tearing resistance parallel to a surface.

With the exploding cartridge, If a chamber hole is drilled centered in the steel bar, we will have a tensile strength critical area made up of the two areas of steel on either side of the chamber. The equivalent force of the exploding cartridge is then 24,000 p.s.i. Multiplied times the cross sectional area of the cartridge.

.225 x .625 x 24,000 p.s.i. = 3375 lbs.

Steel has a tensile strength of about 30,000 p.s.i.
The area of steel resisting this is 2 x .1375 x 1.25 so multiplying x 30,000 p.s.i. = 10,000 lbs.

Of course the portion of steel directly surrounding the cartridge takes the major force, and the portion ahead of the case allows the force to almost simultaneously deflect direct in line with the bullet path, so a lesser resisting pressure strength requirement is probably more accurate.

Increasing the steel to a 5/8" thickness would be a large safety factor improvement. However, I do think the 1/2" slab thickness is satisfactory and will test it later when the weapon construction has progressed to a point allowing testing.

This discussion gives you some ideas as to the safety considerations of the bar magazine.

****

DO NOT USE STINGER OR CCI HIGHER POWER .22 CARTRIDGES!! USE ONLY STANDARD .22 LONG RIFLE AMMO!! THIS IS A PROTOTYPE RIFLE MEANT FOR STANDARD AMMUNITION.

****

Getting the Steel Materials

You should follow a certain order in building the rifle, certain measurements are critical and based around the barrel diameter. You will need:

- A used .22 barrel at a gun show. Probably about a 20 inch barrel, very typical from older .22 rifles, Stevens, Western Field, J.C. Mossberg, etc.
- A strip of steel 1/4" thickness, 2" wide and approx. 12 inches long,
- Also a similar strip in 3/16" thickness,
- Some 2" wide x 12" strips of sheet steel approximately 12 ga. thick.
- For the receiver portion you will need about 14 ga. steel, approx 4 inches wide and 30 inches long.
- And of course a 4 ½ inch wide by ½ inch thick Steel bar from which you can cut several magazine bars.
- Two steel shaft couplers with inner bore   sufficient to slip over your rifle barrel.
- Obtain the following packaged compression springs from Amazon.com or Graingers Supply or some similar industrial jobber. In general Stainless Steel is the best choice and   .035 and larger diameter wire will be desired for strong (approx. 5 lbs per inch) springs, and lighter gauges for lesser strengths. Keep this in mind, and search for lengths you will need.
- For Detent ball, Small Parts Inc. part # CSXX-0150-02 (.300OD x .038WD x .813 FL PK/2) (Amazon.com)
- For Hammer, Small Parts Inc. get Part # CSX-0185-05 (.360OD x .042WD x 2.FL PK/5), also # CSX-0155-05 (.300OD x .038WD x 1.5FL PK/5), CSMW-0160-02

(.360 OD x.032WD x 1.5FL PK/2) and CSMW-0135-05, (.300OD x .035WD x 1.5FL PK/5) (Amazon.com)

- For Trigger Spring and for Positioner "T" assembly, Get Ace Hardware Assortment of compression Springs, # 5213517, a good assortment of low strength units.
- Get a strip of thin steel strapping used to strap items to industrial pallets, etc. usually can find from a lumber yard, a foot is all you will need, ask if you can pick up a piece from the yard. Probably the lighter types.
- Get a high quality #1 High Speed Steel drill bit in the shorter Screw Machine machinist length from a good supplier. I found my bits at a reasonable price from **Associated Industrial Distributors** on the internet.

- Go to a bicycle shop and get a couple of precision 5/16" steel ball bearings.

You will need a few small washers, and some 4-40 and 6-32 screws in various lengths, with smooth washers, lock washers and nuts.

For the Double Action setup you will need some small brass, Aluminum or Steel spacers or rollers. These are available from Electronic and hardware suppliers.

The first part to make, for either a double or single action weapon is the Bar Magazine.

Chapter 5

Fabricating the
Bar Magazine

The critical part of the magazine construction comes in drilling the chamber holes for the cartridges. These must be done very carefully; they must be the correct distance apart, and centered perfectly in the bar. The entire assembly and functioning of the firearm relies on the accuracy established here, it is critical to do a careful job.

In drilling these chamber holes, a very handy accessory is a machine vise with precision X-Y adjustment. Or at the very least, use considerable care in this job.

The holes must be parallel to the sides of the steel, and centered. They must be parallel in the other direction as well, to the end or bottom of the bar. They must enter the barrel in a fairly perfect plane to the axis of the barrel.

I would suggest having the 1/2" bar cut to the 1 1/4" width at a fabrication shop, this is a very thick piece, but they can do it accurately. *It would be a good idea to check with a gunsmith to be sure the steel you have is adequate for this purpose.*

You can always do fine grinding or filing to smooth or true the edges. If you make two to four, those will be you eventual magazines. If you are very careful in construction you will have a few magazines from this process.

The spacing between chamber holes is critical and essentially dependent on barrel diameter. So, prior to drilling your bar magazine you must have your gun barrel.

The spring and ball detent chamber positioning must allow spacing to lock one chamber hole as the other aligns perfectly to the barrel. Thus barrel radius sets the absolute <u>minimum</u> spacing.

In my case, a .22 barrel was found that allows a .400 space between each hole. That is excellent as it allowed a 10 shot bar. *I believe 0.400 should be the minimum attempted with scrap steel. I even had to grind a small amount off the edge of the barrel to fit. I believe this is the minimum possible with available gun barrels and also less spacing might become a safety issue. Keep in mind the detent ball is 5/16" diameter.*

If a gun manufacturer were making the rifle, he would have special steels available that could allow smaller, lighter construction with perfect safety, but we do not have that option.

Note the short depth hole in the Bar Magazine above the upper drilled chamber hole; this is the last detent hole to hold the magazine in place for the last shot. It is the same diameter as each chamber hole, and is spaced above the top chamber hole consistent to hold the correct barrel alignment for the last shot.

The hole diameter is achieved with a #1 H.S.S Drill bit. This bit is .235" diameter. Use the shorter machinist bits, being shorter than normal lengths, they resist bending during drilling operations. The first partial hole can be quite close to the top of the magazine bar. It is only for alignment and has no pressure consideration from a cartridge. If it is very close, operating the gun mechanism after the last shot will eject the bar magazine from the weapon. That is partly the purpose of the extra amount of movement allowed over and above the chamber spacing in determining the positioner setup discussed later.

See Figure 3. This shows the general view of the piece, with straight through chamber holes drilled in the center of the 1/2" width. The clearance distance between holes must allow the 5/16" detent ball to seat in one hole as the one below lines up with the barrel bore.

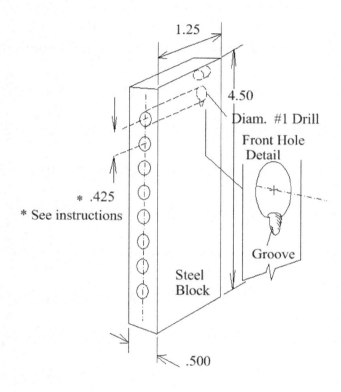

Fig. 3. Gun Magazine

The Templet

Wear your Safety Glasses! Cut a 1/4" thick piece of steel approx 6" long and the width of the magazine bar; (you can make it slightly wider and carefully grind it to match the width.) This

21

forms a templet pattern piece.

You can ideally have this piece sheared at a fabrication shop, or cut it yourself using an Angle Grinder and cutoff disc; <u>be extremely careful with this tool</u>, **use a face shield and ear and breathing protection**- the disk is spinning at several thousand R.P.M. Do not put your face or body in line with the spinning disk! Hold the tool firmly and do not twist it while making a cut. Have the workpiece <u>securely clamped</u>. DO NOT wear long sleeves or any clothing which could snag the spinning disc!

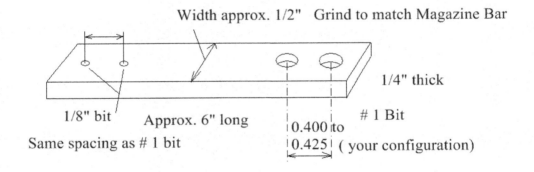

Width approx. 1/2"   Grind to match Magazine Bar

1/4" thick

1/8" bit   Approx. 6" long   # 1 Bit

0.400 to

Same spacing as # 1 bit   0.425 (your configuration)

Fig. 4. Templet

Do final grinding to fit the templet to the precise width of your magazine bar thickness.

Now mark the templet precisely with a center punch centered and at a point about 1/2" from one end as shown in Figure 4, then clamp the piece into the drill press vise, and use a 1/8" High

Speed Steel bit very carefully in the drill press to make the first small drilled indent in the bar at the first location. Whenever you tighten a bit into the chuck, use all three chuck key holes to incrementally tighten the chuck. If you only use one, you will find the bit is not truly tight. Take pains here to do an accurate job, you want these holes precisely in the center and the correct distance apart. Remember to oil the bit to provide cooling and lubrication, and apply a light pressure to just drill an indent into the piece. Drill the 1/8" hole.

Switch to the other end of the templet and carefully do another centered punch mark as you had done the first time. Take the same care with accuracy here as with the first hole. First drill with the 1/8" bit then swap to the #1 bit and drill the final hole making sure to maintain accuracy. When using the #1 bit use perhaps two separate short press sessions, and apply oil in between to drill all the way through the 1/4" steel.

Once you drill these end holes, remove the piece, wipe it clean; next you must measure for the detent hole. Clamp the piece flat in a vise and run a cleaning rod through the rifle barrel and the end hole in the templet.

Sit the 5/16" ball next to the barrel as it sits on the templet... allow a small clearance, and mark the spacing-- approx 0.400 to 0.500" is probably a close bet. This is a fairly simple way to insure the spacing and location of each chamber hole is precisely where it belongs.

Using a center punch, centered perfectly, mark for the detent hole at each end of your templet. Mount the templet in the drill press vise again. Next, carefully align for the second hole, which you marked based on the barrel diameter and 5/16" detent ball... Use the 1/8" bit for the one end, then use the same procedure to do the larger hole at the other end: the 1/8" bit initially then use the #1 High Speed Steel bit to drill the final of the two precise holes centered and the correct distance apart in the templet bar. Your templet should appear as in Figure 4.

This templet will allow you to correctly configure for the precise chamber holes you will later drill in the magazine chamber bar exactly where they belong.

Take extreme care in making the templet accurately. Once this is done, you can place the templet over the edge of the bar magazine, clamp it in a machine vise on the drill press, and drill one precise centered hole at the location of the first detent of the magazine bar. This hole can be fairly close to the top edge of the magazine bar, with the edge of the hole within 3/32 inch; it will also only be about ¼ inch deep as it is only to allow the detent ball to hold the bar for the final round. Drill it with the 1/8" H.S.S. Bit.

Alignment

The technique used to drill the remaining holes is simple but critical; it is done in two steps, first with the 1/8" drill for only about 1/4" depth, then after all start holes are drilled in the bar magazine with the 1/8" bit, the final holes are done with the #1 bit using the 1/8" start holes as an assist in centering. .

Use the first 1/8" hole in the end of the templet with an extra 1/8" bit to align to the first hole you drilled and show the position for the next hole. Then once sure of correct templet centering and alignment, drill a start hole for the next hole in the bar magazine.

****

Now comes a critical item. Suppose although the spacing is good from the last hole, your first chamber hole is a few thousands off from centerline. If you continued this procedure, you would possibly be adding to the error on each succeeding hole! But if you turn the templet over on each succeeding hole, the error should go back and forth around the centerline of the bar... this is the procedure you should use, it will cause the error to fluctuate from centerline but never accumulate.

Assuming a small error, perhaps 5 to 10 thousandths, that seems to be a reasonable acceptable amount... the barrel entrance hole will be reamed to form a conical opening to allow for some misalignment ... the bullet will essentially be nudged and guided into true alignment as it moves into the barrel.

****

Once you have done the remaining 1/8" holes, switch to the #1 H.S.S. Short Bit. Use the bit to carefully drill the first top bar hole about 1/4" deep

Proceed to use the #1 H.S.S. Short Bit and a used empty .22 casing: the casing is placed in the previous drilled hole as a guide and the #1 bit is in the Drill Press Chuck. The drill table vise is loosened, and the .22 casing is inserted partially down into the first templet hole as it is placed on top of the magazine bar in the drill press vise, then slide the templet to allow the casing to slip into the already drilled previous detent hole in the magazine bar.

Clamp the templet and magazine bar together in the drill press vise to lock the alignment. Then carefully align the chucked drill bit into the other templet hole. This locates the next chambering point.. once you do so, carefully clamp the piece in the vise, rechecking to maintain alignment as you carefully tighten the vise. Try to achieve a slight clearance feel all round the bit. Run the drill up and down a couple times to see that alignment is good, that the bit does not bump at one edge.

Observe the bit as the drill contacts the steel... if it bends or distorts realign and retry. If it does not distort, carefully drill the hole doing about 1/4" or less incremental steps, keep lubricating at each step before proceeding. Drill clear through the magazine bar. This completes the first chamber hole. Drill the remaining holes in the same manner, turning the templet over after each hole. My bar allowed for ten chamber holes and one additional detent.

You may wish to grind a *very slight* sloped indent into the lower edge of each chamber hole, a slight gully to help the detent ball roll into the chamber hole. Do not grind too wide or you may have a sloppy grab in the detent. Also use your Dremel tool to grind a slight "gully" down the front center of the magazine bar for the detent to guide into.

NOTE: Because drill ridges in the Bar Magazine will prevent casings from simply falling out after firing, you may decide to have a gunsmith ream the correct holes for .22 cartridges. He can also verify the adequacy of your steel bar.
In a drilled version you must drive the fired casings out, not difficult but just an irritation perhaps.
****

REMEMBER, DO NOT USE STINGER OR CCI HIGHER POWER .22 CARTRIDGES!! USE ONLY STANDARD .22 LONG RIFLE AMMO!! (Peters, Federal, Remington...)
****

Fig. 5. Finished Bar Magazine

Chapter 6

Receiver Housing

For the receiver portion you will need 14 ga. steel, approx 4 ¼ inches wide and perhaps 30 inches long. From the piece you will make cuts as shown to give you the two (left and right) sides of the receiver.

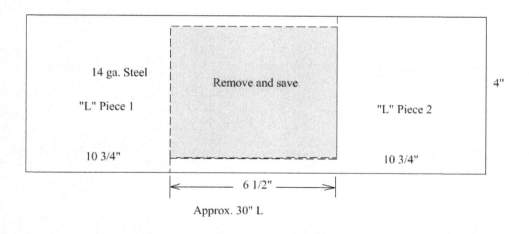

Fig. 6. Receiver Cuts

Wear your Safety glasses or face shield! Use the Angle Grinder with cutting disk to cut the pieces, then grind the edges to carefully remove burrs and make the pieces identical.

Next we will make the parts which attach inside the receiver sides as guides for the bar magazine. These pieces when mounted will be slightly higher than the 1/2" magazine bar so that it can slide freely with no interference. You must do grinding to make just a slight clearance for the magazine, perhaps 1/64".

The front piece shown in Figure 7 is 12 ga. steel with two holes at the same spacing as the chamber holes in the bar magazine.

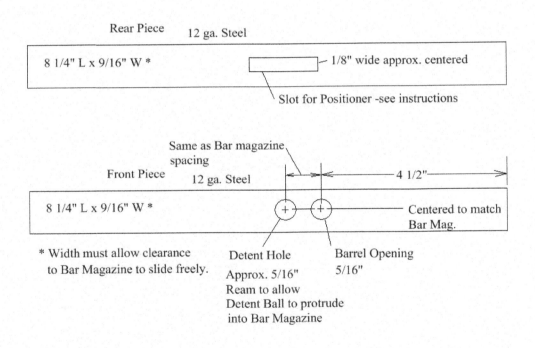

Rear Piece   12 ga. Steel

8 1/4" L x 9/16" W *

1/8" wide approx. centered

Slot for Positioner -see instructions

Same as Bar magazine spacing

Front Piece   12 ga. Steel

8 1/4" L x 9/16" W *

4 1/2"

Centered to match Bar Mag.

* Width must allow clearance to Bar Magazine to slide freely.

Detent Hole
Approx. 5/16"
Ream to allow
Detent Ball to protrude
into Bar Magazine

Barrel Opening
5/16"

Fig. 7. Magazine Guide Plates

One hole will be for the detent ball to lock the bar magazine, the other will be the barrel opening where the barrel aligns. The barrel opening will be 5/16". The detent hole should be drilled with a 19/64" H.S. Steel bit... and carefully reamed so that the steel ball bearing will be locked with a significant portion poking through to lock the bar magazine. Ream carefully, testing after a couple minor turns as you get close to size... approximately 3/32" of ball inside the bar magazine area is what you wish to achieve. It must be enough to firmly lock the magazine as it lodges in each chamber hole.

The rear Magazine Guide has a small slot milled into it to allow the Positioner Bar to fit inside and move the magazine chambers into each locking position. This slot should be about 0.1 to 0.125 inch wide and length approximately the distance between chambers plus about 1/4 inch.

The Dremel tool with small cutting disks is used along with a drill bit to form the slot, first drilling about three holes, centered in the strip, one at each end of the desired slot, and one between. Then the piece is clamped in a vise and a cutting disk is used to cut between the holes. Be sure to wear protective eye glasses and a dust mask here, the disk is small and delicate, but cuts the steel very well. Hold the tool steadily bracing on something and apply a small force, cutting slowly and cautiously; the disks are fragile. Don't be too concerned if you break one or two, this is likely, they are very fragile. Once you have achieved the cuts, the slot will need some gentle grinding and filing to even the sides and square the ends of the slot. You can use a small grinding wheel in the Dremel tool and a file to achieve this.
****

Before doing this next portion, you may want to consider widening the receiver space to the rear of the firing pin area as I mention later in Chapter 14, *though I did my entire rifle in approximately the 1/2" spacing.* Sometimes the narrow spacing made it difficult to fit springs and parts with a floating clearance to minimize friction. But it can be done, just that it might be easier with a wider gap between the receiver sides. Gives you another choice, changes nothing but the width.

****

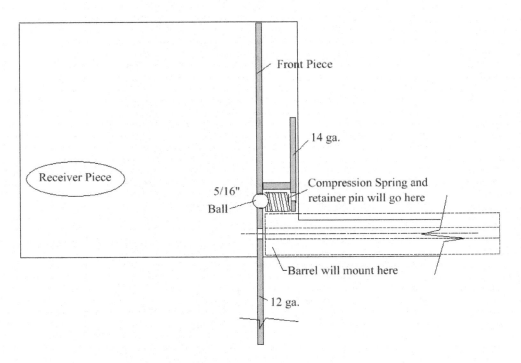

Fig. 8. Welding for Front
Magazine Guide

It is now time to assemble the pieces to hold the Bar Magazine and help form the Receiver assembly of your gun. I recommend tack welding the front piece onto the left receiver plate so that the detent ball and associated compression spring will be accessible and mount from the front. The detent ball should protrude into the space to eventually house the Bar Magazine. **Since you should have carefully reamed the detent hole already you**

should cover it as well as the barrel hole with a scrap of metal before you weld. Otherwise, weld spatter could shoot beads of molten metal into those holes, damaging them.

Clamp the front guide piece about 3/4" back from the front of the main receiver surface area with the barrel tab sticking forward. (The barrel tab will allow clamping of the barrel during later assembly and fabrication.) Align the barrel hole close to the bottom about 3/8" to 1/2" from the edge as shown in Figure 8. Lay a scrap metal piece over the holes you have drilled and tack weld the assembly carefully to be straight upright.

When welding an upright piece onto a flat portion, try to slightly tilt the vertical piece away from the side you will apply the fillet welds on, as the welds cool they will pull the piece slightly as the hot weld cools, straightening it . Practice on some scrap until you feel confident.

Protect the barrel and detent holes with a scrap of metal, then weld a couple small ½ inch high 14 ga. braces perpendicular to form an upper containment for the spring that will hold the detent ball in place. See Figure 8. Leave a space at the top front portion of the receiver back plate... this will be for a later barrel brace.

Drill a small hole in the front spring retainer to allow for a pin to retain the spring. You may tap it for a 4-40 screw if you wish. You should have already reamed the detent ball hole but carefully clean it in case some weld beads or debris spattered inside.

Next prepare the rear magazine guide. Weld two small 3/16" thick mounting tabs onto the rear magazine guide, one very near the top and one approximately 1 ½ inch down from the top of the rear guide; the purpose is to drill these tabs and use two 6-32 screws to mount the rear guide as you align and fit it to the inserted magazine. See Figure 9.

Load the magazine bar with ten empty fired .22 casings and place it on the back receiver plate, against the front magazine guide with the casing rims facing to the rear.   Place the rear magazine guide in place, allow a very slight sliding clearance to the rims, approximately 1/64 inch. Slide the magazine so that a chamber aligns with the front guide barrel opening and place the 5/16" detent ball in place with your finger, so that it protrudes into the next chamber hole just above the barrel opening chamber. It should readily protrude inside the magazine space and slip right into the next chamber hole above with the lower hole in alignment with the barrel hole.

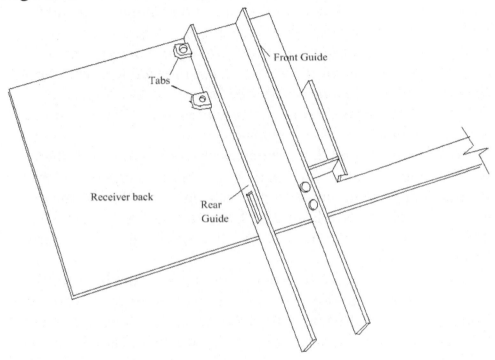

Fig. 9. Rear Guide Installation

In this position, look at the rear guide slot, the top of the cartridge rim aligned with the barrel hole should just be visible at the bottom of the slot. Slide the rear guide until it is in this position with about 1/16" of the cartridge rim showing. As you observe this position of the cartridge aligned with the barrel, carefully pick the spot for a firing pin to strike the rim of the cartridge at the point it is closest to the receiver plate. Mark that point very carefully on the rear guide. Drill it with a 3/32" bit. Verify that it is in the correct spot as you recheck the rear guide.

Weld a 3/16" piece of steel about 1/2" x 1" onto the rear guide over the area of the cartridge rim below the slot and on the rear side of the guide. This provides a strengthened area behind the cartridge. Grind if necessary to match to the rear guide sides. Then using the existing firing pin hole on the magazine side of the guide, drill from the front surface on through the 3/16" reinforcement. Verify that this is aligned with the lower edge of the cartridge rim once more.

With the parts properly positioned, mark and drill the two mounting tab holes in the left receiver plate for 6-32 screw clearance. (A 9/64" bit...)

This establishes the rear guide fairly accurately.

Mount the rear guide and check the clearance to the magazine bar, the firing pin hole alignment, etc.... check carefully. You are now ready for the remaining mechanism.

The following photo in Figure 10 reveals some of the construction. (There may be some additional assembly, I often was trying things out beyond the chapters.)

Fig. 10. Magazine Guides

34

Chapter 7

Spring and Mechanism
for
Single Action

The single action mechanism is fairly simple, as you cock it manually each shot.

There are a few critical item to proper function though,

- Spring strength
- Cocking motion must also seat round
- A suitable link may be needed to simultaneously cock the mechanism after the round is seated

I did not have an idea what force it took to fire a .22 cartridge, so I unloaded a .22 revolver and tried measuring the force of the hammer. A spring characteristic is typically defined as lbs per inch of deflection. I just sort of guessed maybe 5 to 10 lb/in. It turned out a 5 lb. weight cocked the hammer just fine.

So by picking a spring that provides about 3 to 5 lbs of force per inch with perhaps an inch or two of cocking movement gives a rough objective for the force and motion required. This amount of spring constant is actually fine, next, the motion and distance required to position a cartridge prior to impact and firing of the cartridge is needed.

See Figure 11 below. This is a rough visualization of a possible gun mechanism. The "T" assembly and detent ball is a very reliable way to position each chamber. A light spring is used at the top to insure correct return of the positioner for the next chambering motion. It must return the positioner *above* the next cartridge rim every time. One more spring device is used to gently press the positioner against the bar magazine to insure catching the rim of each cartridge.

A "T" was an easier path to a future double action mechanism, but actually for the single action, an inverted "L" shape could also work nicely.

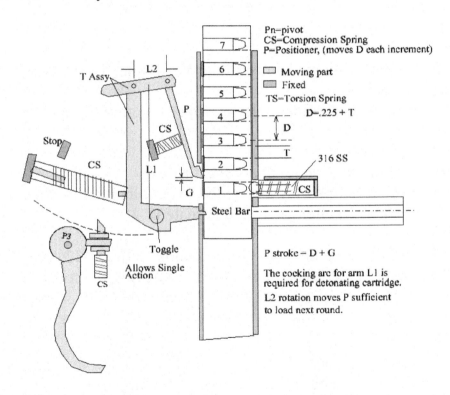

Fig. 11. General Single Action

In building the firearm for this book, I often ran into difficulties in making the parts or making them work smoothly in the way I visualized. Sometimes a simple change in direction makes fabrication much easier!

****

Anytime you use a guide rod for a spring, I learned the end that is pinned <u>should not be on a moving part</u>. For example, do not pin the long guide on the hammer spring at the hammer end. If you do, as the hammer swings the guide moves taking up additional free space you may need for some other function. *A very simple principle, but keep it in mind.*

****

Making a good firing pin setup, is probably the most critical part of all after the bar magazine. With care, a one-piece bolt or hammer/firing pin unit might be fine without the added complexity of the floating firing pin. But for a simpler alignment a floating firing pin as shown is a good choice.

This is because, a .22 cartridge is rimfire so the tolerance in placement of the firing pin is very critical, and it is easier to uses a floating pin. The whole setup is dependent on the accuracy of your bar magazine, and flatness of the receiver, everything! So, take your time doing a good job. (I saw from this that a centerfire design would be a lot easier, perhaps in .380 or 9mm caliber.) A centerfire cartridge has a large primer area, much larger than a .22 rimfire.

Note the D + G measurement in Figure 11. You must take this measurement on your own bar magazine; the movement required is the distance between chamber holes plus perhaps 1/16 to 1/10" ... the mechanism positioner bar "P" must be gapped to move a bit before it begins to engage the rim of the cartridge -this is to allow sufficient movement to position a cartridge and return with adequate clearance to grab the next cartridge.

The steel assembly can be somewhat shaped like an inverted "T" to provide a lower control arm and an upper arm to operate the positioner to push the next cartridge into firing position. The pivot point is roughly where the two arms come together at the apex. Initially you can have two pieces of say 3/16" steel as the main upper piece, and a piece of 14 ga. sandwiched as the lower arm.

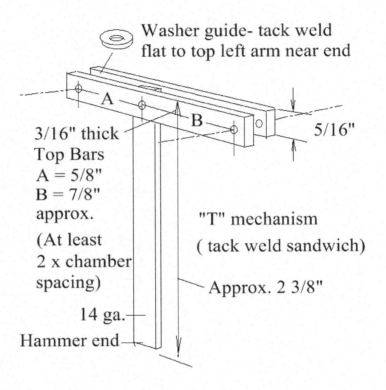

Washer guide- tack weld
flat to top left arm near end

A

B

3/16" thick
Top Bars
A = 5/8"
B = 7/8"
approx.

(At least
2 x chamber
spacing)

14 ga.

Hammer end

5/16"

"T" mechanism
(tack weld sandwich)

Approx. 2 3/8"

Fig. 12. "T" Assembly

A ratio of arm lengths will determine the action: On each cocking motion, which must provide hammer spring tension sufficient to fire a cartridge, the distance the hammer moves must simultaneously produce the required positioner movement. As long as the hammer movement is enough to compress a spring for firing, and the ratio of upper to lower "T" arm is correct, the two different movements may be coordinated, even though they are unequal. The hammer may need to move two or three times as far as the positioner to cock, but it doesn't matter; the selection of arm ratio can match the two operations.

Because the upper portion of the "T" piece pivots near its center, it is sandwiched thicker so as to be more stable; the lower arm will not wobble as badly. This is desired as we wish the hammer to "float" not rub on the receiver side panels.

Figure 12 shows the "T" bar for my rifle, but slight dimension variations may be required depending on your chamber spacing! When the positioner that ratchets the bar magazine is at its lowest point in the rear guide slot, the right "T" arm should be directly in line with the positioner. This determines the lowest movement of the positioner. When the "T" bar lower arm is essentially vertical about its pivot, the positioner should be about 1/16" to 1/10" above the cartridge rim that will next advance downward. This requires the "B" distance in Figure 12 to increase slightly as your chamber spacing increases,. *As a rule of thumb, "B" should be about twice your chamber spacing.*

Use Safety Glasses or a face shield! Cut the parts for the "T" unit as shown in Figure 12. Temporarily tack weld your "T" piece together as shown being sure to allow sufficient "B" space. Lay the "T" piece on top of your bottom receiver piece, and visualize it pivoting and operating a thin positioner piece which will push the bar magazine to align each chamber. The positioner piece must clear your mounting screws on the rear magazine guide, and enter the slot to accomplish moving the bar magazine on each shot. There must be some clearance above the "T" to allow for the spring shown in Figure 11.

Drill the center through hole in the upper bars using a 9/64" bit. (Clearance for a 6-32 machine screw..) Drill the other two holes as clearance for a #5 Box nail, approximately 3/32". Smooth and remove rough edges on the` "T" piece as you go.

39

In placing your parts, and establishing the needed clearances, you will find a good pivot point for the "T" piece... It should be fairly close to the rear magazine guide, but the guide mounting tabs must not interfere with the upper right arm or the magazine positioner. Allow about 1 ¼ inch clearance to the top of the receiver plate to allow for the spring above the "T" arm; my pivot hole was approximately 1 3/4" inches from the left edge of the rear magazine guide proper and 1 1/4" from the upper edge.

But wait until you have done a test of the positioner and "T" assembly specific to your situation, it may be different due to your particular chamber spacing !

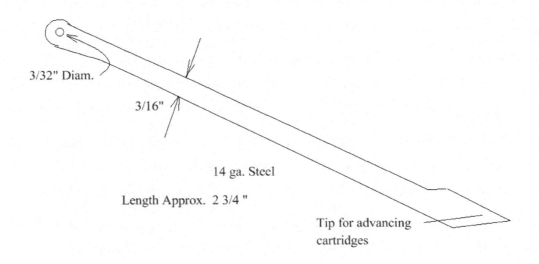

3/32" Diam.

3/16"

14 ga. Steel

Length Approx. 2 3/4 "

Tip for advancing cartridges

Fig. 13. Magazine Positioner

The next piece to make is the positioner; use a narrow strip of 14 ga. steel. You must visualize the length you will need from positioning your own parts, the "T" piece and clearance of your mounting tabs on the rear magazine guide. Make the positioner piece slightly longer, you can grind to fit as you test it. See Figure 13.

You are about to use the Angle Grinder. Put on your face safety shield, and ear protectors and dust mask. *Make sure you do not have any baggy clothing, long sleeves or a power cord in the way, anything that could catch in the cutoff disk of your Angle Grinder. This is a very dangerous tool so read the instructions carefully and be very cautious. Hold it firmly and clamp the "T" piece securely in the bench vise. Avoid placing any part of your body in line with the disk!*

Remove the "T" bar from the receiver and clamp it in a Bench Vise. Using your Angle Grinder, carefully run the cutoff disk slightly in and out of the longer slot of the upper part of the "T" unit to give clearance for the positioner bar to fit freely inside. No excessive grinding, just the minimum to allow the positioner to freely move inside the slot. A swipe or two should achieve this. Clean the metal dust from the part and remove any burrs.

Use a #5 Box nail for the positioner pivot pin, cut the shank end off so the portion with the nail head is about equal to the thickness of the "T" bar and insert through the bar and positioner to give a pin for the operation and checking of the positioner.

Push the bar magazine (always with spent cartridges in place) into the magazine slot so the second chamber anchors at the detent ball. This should place a spent cartridge in line with the barrel. The rim should just be visible above the lower edge of the rear magazine guide slot.

Poke a 6-32 machine screw through the center pivot hole in the upper part of the "T" assembly. Place the "T" and positioner on the bottom (left) receiver panel so that the pivot is about 1 3/4" left of the rear magazine guide and approx. 1 1/4" down from the top of the receiver panel. Hold the screw in position and rotate the "T" to see if the positioner clears the tabs on the

41

rear magazine guide and will reach the bottom of the rear guide slot and cartridge rim when the right arm and positioner are aligned towards the bottom of the slot. Adjust the assembly if needed so the positioner just touches the cartridge. Then rotate the "T" assembly so the lower arm is directly down to see if the positioner can rise above the cartridge above aligned in the detent. You can experiment a bit here, possibly grinding some of the positioner tip off and try again if necessary until you find a satisfactory pivot point on the lower receiver plate.
Locate and drill a 9/64 hole through the bottom receiver plate.

Slide a 3/4" 6-32 screw up through the receiver side panel from the bottom and place a washer and the pivot of the "T" over it. The front and rear magazine guides will be facing up, you can operate the bar magazine and visualize for the remaining construction.

Check that the positioner arm goes into the rear magazine guide slot as you gently operate the "T" assembly, and insure it will go clear to the bottom when rotated. The length of the "T" right arm should be such that the positioner will be bottomed in the slot at the rear magazine guide at the right arm's closest point. In other words, the positioner should reach the bottom of the rear magazine slot when the right arm is essentially in line with the positioner as it touches the bottom.. this is its lowest point.

Testing the Positioner

Insert the 5/16" detent ball into the front magazine guide and install the CSXX-0150-02 spring and another cutoff #5 Box nail or if threaded, a 1/2" 4-40 screw as a retainer for the spring, be sure it is short enough to not interfere with the ball movement. The ball should protrude about 3/32" into the bar magazine area. Lay the receiver assembly flat on a table surface, some papers beneath to protect the surface. Wipe the space between the guides and the bar magazine with a rag making sure it is clean.

Insert the bar magazine with empty fired cartridges at the rear into the space between the guides, it should slide with very minimal sliding clearance; slide it down to the detent ball, and push it so that the first chamber opening pops onto the ball. It should be a secure lock. If you don't feel it is quite enough lock effect, add a small washer spacer or two between the spring and retainer pin at the detent spring until is is a stronger lock.

Next, hold the positioner bar with light pressure into the rear guide slot. Rotate the lower arm of the "T". It should be fitted so that when the lower arm of the "T" is facing down towards the bottom of the receiver, the positioner is about 1/16" above the upper cartridge rim, the one whose chamber is locked by the detent ball. Grind the tip of the positioner if need to accomplish this fit. Once correct it should easily grab against the cartridge rim with a clockwise rotation of the "T" lower arm as light pressure is initially applied against the positioner. As the lower arm is rotated about 40 to 45 degrees clockwise, the positioner should easily ratchet the cartridge and chamber downward until it aligns with the barrel and the chamber above pulls and locks into the detent.

The right "T" arm should be approximately in line with the positioner when it reaches its lowest reach point. Let the "T" assembly rotate back upright so the positioner is once again a bit above the next cartridge. Each repeat should ratchet the magazine bar down one space. If it does this you are ready to complete the spring assemblies. Otherwise, grind or make necessary adjustments to achieve satisfactory operation. If a pivot hole is wrongly placed, you can weld it closed and redo.

Make a small angle bracket of the 14 ga. steel, about 1/2" wide with 1/2" arms. It will mount to support the spring which goes on the positioner. Before bending it drill a 7/64" hole in what will form one leg of the piece. (clearance for a 4-40 screw...)

Remember one item in the parts list was some thin steel banding from pallets... it is a very springy thin steel, and if you bend it you may be able to use it as a spring for the positioner. It has an advantage of allowing the positioner to slide downward while also maintaining a slight pressure against the piece to insure grabbing the rim of the cartridges. An ideal material for this purpose. You can also sand a smooth area onto the positioner piece where it slides against the spring steel. It will make the positioner and spring slide more friction free. And of course later on this surface can have some lubricant.

A note on placement of the L bracket: it must not block the "T" bar action to impede full positioner operation!

Determine a point above the "T" assembly pivot to drill a 3/32" hole to provide the pin for the guide for the upper spring. These steps complete the positioner/ "T" assembly parts.

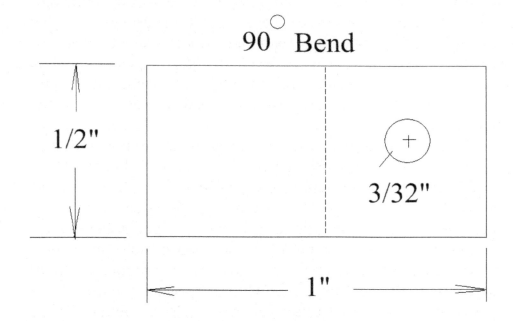

Fig. 14. Bracket

A note on placement of the L bracket: it must not block the "T" bar action to impede full positioner operation!

Determine a point above the "T" assembly pivot to drill a 3/32" hole to provide the pin for the guide for the upper spring. These steps complete the positioner/ "T" assembly parts.

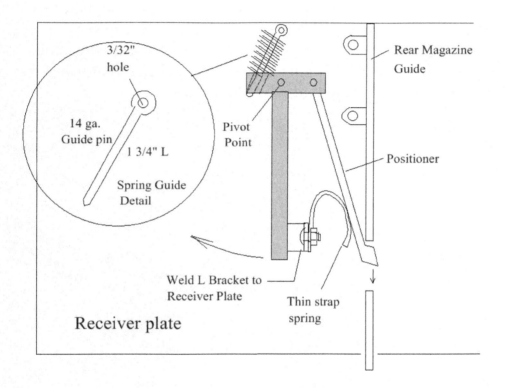

Fig. 15. "T" Assembly Details

See details in Figure 15. Use a fairly weak approx. 3/8" diameter spring from the Ace Hardware assortment for the upper spring, just so it reliably returns the positioner to a spot <u>above</u> the cartridge lined up at the detent ball. If the action appears to need a stronger spring, you can use an inner spring to add to the effect

45

of the other, use a stronger spring, or add a thick spacer between the "T" and spring.

Adjust and correct problems by modifying, grinding, correcting the slot, whatever it takes to obtain reliable operation.

Once you are satisfied, test the bar magazine movement with the detent ratcheting effect of the positioner. Apply some grease to the face of the positioner where it contacts the spring strap.

Figure 16 shows part of my construction; also note the magazine cover tack welded onto the left receiver lower magazine area portion, and the tab at the lower rear magazine guide which is welded to the left receiver panel and allows a 6-32 screw to be threaded into the rear guide.

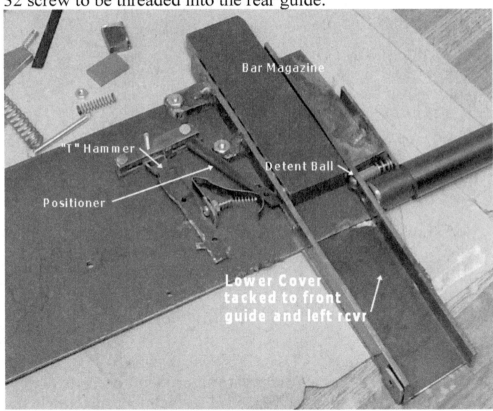

Fig. 16. "T" and Positioner

Hammer-Striker Assembly

The Hammer assembly/firing pin requires care and accuracy. With rimfire cartridges, the area the firing pin must strike is small. So you must have a very precise firing pin arrangement. You can have a floating firing pin with a separate hammer-striker or combine it in one piece. If the striker and firing pin are one piece, you must make this part very carefully. The assembly must operate easily, yet not be so sloppy as to be too loose. Visualize the operation, if the hammer and firing pin are one piece, it would be prudent to have some sort of inclined guides to insure the firing pin guides directly into the firing pin hole in the rear magazine guide. With the "T" assembly and positioner de-scribed, the arc of rotation would require very tricky workman-ship to accomplish that.

But if the firing pin floats, and is held in a guide with a spring loaded clearance gap to hold from striking the cartridge, it can be correctly positioned for firing with a portion of the firing pin already inserted in the firing pin hole of the rear guide. This eliminates the problem of guiding the firing pin into the hole, *it is already partially inside!* Then when the hammer is cocked and released, the floating firing pin is struck by the hammer and the impact drives it forward to fire the cartridge. It then returns to the floating position against a stop, held by its spring.

This is the method I used for the repeater Single Action mech-anism and the later Double Action setup. It has the advantage of having the firing pin already in the firing pin hole, eliminating the problem of a hammer with integral firing pin slightly mis-aligned to the hole. See Figure 17.
This gives a general view of parts for the firing pin block and hammer-striker.
All the hammer-striker has to do is strike the floating firing pin. It should hit the firing pin block in line with the firing pin, not offset.

A safety can be accomplished with this device by blocking movement of the firing pin.

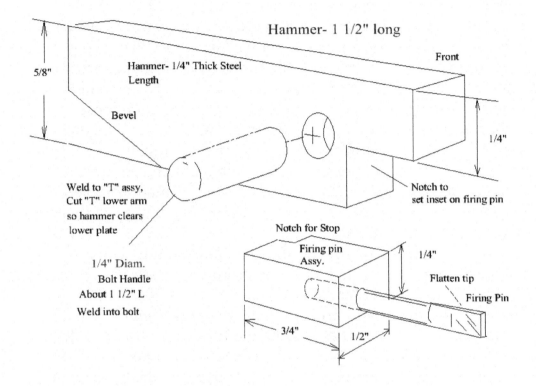

Fig. 17. Hammer and Firing Pin

Cut a strip of 14 ga. steel matched to the width of your rear magazine guide (approx. 9/16") to form part of the lower plate of the receiver. You may cut it larger and grind to match the height of the rear magazine guide. Lightly tack weld this piece to the left receiver side plate as shown. Weld on the outside lower edge, you do not want to damage the inner receiver surface where the trigger will likely mount. Do not weld it to the rear magazine guide, but it should be right against it. Remember to always cover the previous piece to avoid weld spatter on critical surfaces. You want the receiver area and the area where the "T" assembly mounts to remain clean and undamaged.

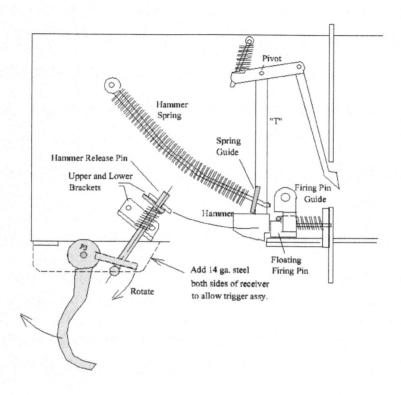

Fig. 18. Gun Assembly

See Figure 18 for a representative diagram. The firing pin must precisely guide to hit the rim of the cartridge. Using the floating firing pin, the guides can be a piece of 14 ga. steel fastened to the one receiver plate, and one guide can be the lower receiver plate, the bottom plate. If you choose rectangular steel pieces for the hammer and floating firing pin, they can easily be made to properly align; the firing pin will lie upon the left receiver plate and the hammer will be welded to the lower part of the "T" assembly, and ideally will float between the left and right receiver plates.

You can carefully grind the firing pin unit to fit so that it can move smoothly but yet be a close tolerance to the housing as well as guide into the firing pin opening. Although the picture shows a thin firing pin, it is a good idea to have it substantial right up almost to the tip. The tip should be rectangular to overlap the rim of the cartridges. The rim is the primer, and you want to be sure to hit this point.

Look closely at Figure 18. Note that there is a pin at the upper left of the firing pin block assembly; with the firing pin guide, it acts as a stop for the floating firing pin, it keeps a portion of the firing pin in the firing pin hole; the firing pin block cannot go back far enough to allow the floating block to fall out of the firing pin hole. The end result is that you want the firing pin to operate perfectly, with minimal friction, and the hammer pivoting around the "T" pivot to swing reliably to initiate the firing pin. The lower receiver piece also stops the hammer-striker at about the same location to help prevent hammer damage to the firing pin stop, but it will still impinge into the firing pin space a bit.

The notch shown in the hammer is cut to accomplish this; providing a partial impact to the firing pin unit, but keeping the hammer short of hitting the firing pin stop.

You need to pick a small diameter spring for the firing pin, one that is not very strong, but when compressed will only allow perhaps 1/16" to 3/32" of firing pin to protrude into the inner magazine area to fire a cartridge. You can check springs from an old ball point pen or perhaps find one in the Ace Hardware assortment. You may need to cut the spring in half with wire nipper pliers.

Also make sure that the hammer hits the firing pin block in line with the firing pin. This prevents the thin pin from being bent by an off centered strike point.

You should make the floating firing pin about ¼ to ½ the weight of the hammer head, essentially size wise proportion is a good estimate. The hammer-striker will move slower but on impact will impart a higher velocity to the firing pin to fire the cartridge.

Because the firing pin hole in the rear magazine guide is close to the receiver plate, not centered, the floating firing pin block of steel it is embedded into and epoxied must be custom fit with care.

Fig. 19. Piece of Original Barrel
Use a thin piece of the original steel barrel or receiver that was

attached to your barrel as a hard portion for the actual firing pin.

Figure 19 shows the portion of barrel breech I cut off my used .22 barrel. It had quite a bit of quality steel that could be used for a firing pin. You will do most of the cutting of that original barrel receiver piece with a hacksaw to avoid overheating and losing the temper. Cut a long narrow strip of metal about 1/8" diameter and ¾ to 1 inch long.... whatever shape that will give you a straight metal strip to fit to the firing pin block after filing and grinding.

The rear tip can be epoxied into the rest of the firing pin assembly once you have determined the final shape. The assembly will be sandwiched together as needed. Leave a fair length on the pin itself as it should partially fall inside the firing pin hole in the rear guide. Before you build the remainder of the guide for the firing pin, you must first lay the small piece of floating firing pin block flat on your left receiver plate with the filed and shaped piece of firing pin in the rear guide hole.

****

NOTE: You may need to temporarily remove the rear magazine guide and slightly drill and wobble a bit in the firing pin hole to elongate it to accommodate the rectangular tip of the firing pin! The tip must move freely into the firing pin hole; file the tip as needed but maintain a rectangular shape, elongate the hole as needed.

****

Place the floating block against the receiver bottom plate. You must carefully mark the point where the pin should attach to your floating block, keep the pin level to the receiver surface and straight into the block. This device is shown back in Figure 17.

Once marked, drill a 1/4" to 3/8" deep hole into the little block, use about a 1/8" bit depending on the diameter of the base of your firing pin piece. Determine a point at the upper left corner of the firing pin block for the stop with the firing pin still partially inside the firing pin hole of the rear magazine guide and being held by the spring. Keep this point in mind.

Recheck that the block with pin now will guide into the firing pin hole without hangup. Check that when pushed against the spring the pin can slip into the magazine bar area enough to fire a cartridge. File if necessary. Make sure it fits easily and will go into the magazine area enough to fire a cartridge.

At this point it is a good idea to harden the firing pin, it needs to be tough so as not to bend and hard enough at the tip to withstand the impact of firing a cartridge.

Hardening the Firing Pin

Home hardening and tempering is accomplished in two steps. Read about hardening and tempering on the Internet first. Basically it can be done as a two step process: heating the metal red hot, then doing a quench in motor oil, followed by a lower temperature period quench or a slow oven process.

Be safe --- wear safety glasses and leather gloves, do the actual process outside if possible and have a metal plate or tin panel available to cover the oil quench in case it flares up or tries to catch fire.

Have a small can with some motor oil, like a tuna can. Keep a metal panel close to cover it in case it wants to catch fire . First you grip the firing pin at the rear end in Vise-Grip Pliers, and use a Propane Torch to heat the very tip and front portion of the firing pin until it glows red hot, then quickly drop it into the small tin can of motor oil. Because the pin itself is so small, it will only take a few seconds to become red hot. The oil contains Carbon, which absorbs into the surface of the Steel, providing a molecular hardening at the surface. Pick the pin out of the oil after a bit with a small pliers. Be careful as it may be brittle at this stage.

The next part can be done in an oven or as recommended in internet articles. In my case I placed the firing pin in the oven on a small tin can and left it at about 300 to 350 degrees for an hour or so. Then allow the small piece to cool.

This process should give a good surface hardness, but also a toughness to the pin. It will handle the impact of hitting the cartridges just fine. Without this step, bending and mushrooming of the pin upon repetitive impact with the cartridges will occur.

Do one last check of the fit of the firing pin and block. If it looks fine mix and put some epoxy into the floating block hole and push the pin into it. Sit upright and allow to dry.

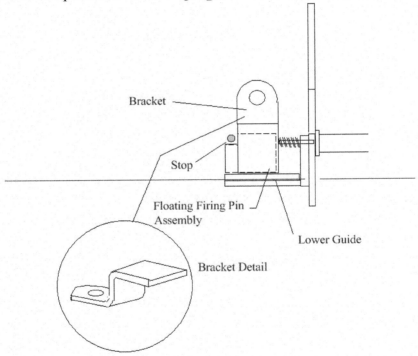

Fig. 20. Firing Pin Guide

See Figure 20. This shows the guide for the firing pin. You will bend this from 14 ga. steel strip, and it must not bind the firing pin block, only contain it. If the guide is too loose at the flat facing surface, you can weld a bump on the rear and grind until it is suitable … providing a smooth guide for the firing pin block unit. Mark and drill to mount the guide. Drill for a 6-32 clearance. Or you can weld the guide onto the lower (left) receiver.

Determine the position for the stop pin to allow the assembly to be slightly restrained just inside the firing pin hole. Mark and drill a 3/32"hole, and tap for a 4-40 screw run up through the hole. Or you may use a bit of #5 nail; tack weld it on the outside of the left receiver plate. Either mounting can work, your choice.

Once you are satisfied with the movement and fit of the firing pin assembly, you can make the hammer-striker piece. The mechanism to operate the positioner will eventually be controlled by the hammer-striker operation.

Remove the "T" assembly and weld the steel hammer-striker to the bottom of the "T" bar; position it at a spot so it will strike the firing pin block but still allow full positioner action. It should go far enough forward to move the firing pin just into the magazine area, but the bottom receiver piece should stop the hammer before it hits the firing pin stop. The firing pin stop may actually be placed anywhere it does not interfere with the hammer movement.

The next thing is to fit the right side of the receiver and test the bolt/firing pin mechanism to establish for mounting the trigger.

Check that the firing pin coming through the rear magazine guide will impinge on the rim of a used cartridge in the bar magazine, but is normally backed into the firing pin hole prior to firing. Remember, the spring used should be fairly weak, but should not allow more than maybe 3/32" intrusion of firing pin into the magazine area.

You must weld raised fastening bosses (raised surfaces) onto the lower (left) receiver panel. There will be at least four places where the receiver plates should fasten. One point, "C" along with the pivot point for the "T" piece will not have a boss but will be be drilled to match on both receiver panels.

Make three 1/4" thick steel pieces of the same height as the front and rear magazine guides. The guides themselves serve as spacers too. Protect the existing receiver panel with a piece of scrap metal or cardboard and weld two bosses at the approximate places shown in Figure 21 so as to clear your mechanism. Save the remaining boss for later after determining the hammer-striker release.

Remove screws from the left receiver panel so that you can lay the right receiver piece directly under for drilling matching holes. Do this carefully on the drill press. Take the upper right receiver piece and place it under the left receiver piece upon which you had mounted the "T" and other items.

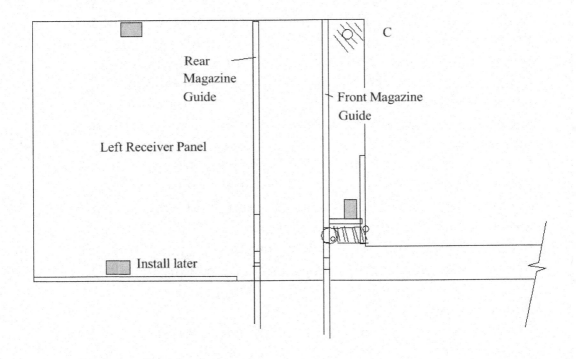

Fig. 21. Support Points

56

Upper (Right) Receiver Plate

Clamp and drill the hole for the "T" pivot and hole "C" to match on the two receiver side panels.

Next, take the left receiver panel with the bosses and carefully mark and drill a 9/64" (6-32 clearance ...) hole through the center each boss on the drill press. Now clamp the two receiver plates together, With the right receiver on the bottom, aligning the "C" and "T" pivot holes, the left receiver piece on top; drill through the two installed bosses to make matching holes in the right receiver panel. Now the two panels should be matched to fit together.

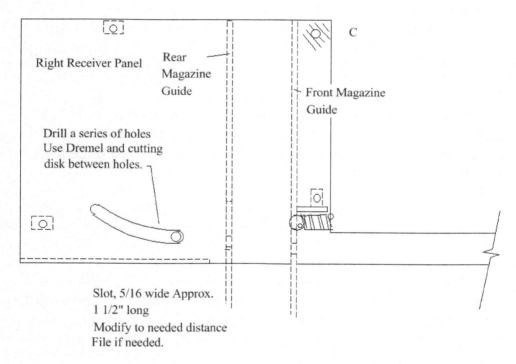

Fig. 22. Hammer Toggle Slot

Cutting the Hammer Toggle Slot

The right receiver panel must now be cut to allow for cocking the hammer. To cut a slot like this, you determine the location and drill a series of holes, then use a hacksaw and the Dremel type rotary tool with a cutting disk to cut between the holes.

Because the slot must match to your rifle setup, your measurements will set up the slot dimensions. Figure 22 gives you an idea.... using the right position of the hammer as a starting reference, draw the arc pivoting around the "T" pivot point; measure and drill a series of adjoining 5/16" holes to the left for about 2 3/8".

Use safe practice, face shield, ear protection and dust mask when using the Dremel, remember the cutting disks can disintegrate in an instant... Clamp the piece in a vise and hold the tool very carefully, be safe.

You may cut some of this rough with a Hacksaw blade if the holes join each other. Finish with a round file and some careful grinding. Later you may add more slot arc if needed once tests are completed.

Spring Setup
and Hammer Release

After filing and grinding, temporarily mount the right receiver panel and check that the Toggle handle/hammer can be pulled back as desired past a point where the positioner will successfully position the magazine bar, repeatedly ratcheting it down one chamber on each motion.

If action seems satisfactory, remove the right panel. Temporarily remove the "T" hammer assembly and grind a bevel on the lower left (rear) of the hammer-striker while you have it out. This is to allow the hammer to slide past the hammer latch, deflecting it until the latch grabs as the front of the hammer passes.

Cut a small strip of 14 ga. steel and bend to form a spring guide eyelet slot when welded to the lower portion of the "T" assembly hammer arm. Weld the slightly offset eyelet tab at the rear of the lower hammer arm; this will form the guide slot on the hammer for the long hammer spring guide. Grind off excess weld metal and deburr. Make a thin spring guide about 4 1/2" long with an eyelet at the upper end drilled with a 7/64" bit, which will be pinned in the upper receiver area. Grind it narrow over its entire remaining length, perhaps to about 1/10" width. Twist the spring guide 90 degrees near the upper fastening eyelet so the wide part of the guide will end up crosswise between the two receiver sides, thus limiting side play of the spring. You next want to slightly bend the guide into an arc similar to the path the hammer will swing. The guide should slip through the welded tab on the upper rear of the lower "T" arm and guide just past the side of the lower arm as the hammer swings back..

Loosen the "T" assembly pivot bolt and rotate the hammer assembly loosely forward against the firing pin block. Slide a small washer and the 2" heavy Stainless Steel spring type CSX-0185-05 onto the spring guide. Place another identical spring onto the guide, (or a second small washer, if you wish to use a spring similar in diameter to the heavier initial spring) perhaps in a *slightly lighter wire gauge* … the idea is to get approximately 4" of total spring length, get a spring movement sufficient to give about a 1 1/2" displacement of the hammer, with suitable spring energy to fire a cartridge. The CSX-0185-05 spring is approximately .042 diameter wire and 5 lbs per inch of compression. As you go down in wire diameter say .035 to .038, the springs are more flexible but slightly weaker. *Make sure that the washer is only slightly larger than the spring, it should not drag against the receiver side panels.* Another good spring choice is the CSMW-0135-05, a .300 OD x .035 WD x 1.5L spring.

Slide the guide into the hammer eyelet and alongside one side of the lower "T" arm, (whichever side accommodates the previously mentioned offset..) then mount the eyelet end to the upper receiver temporarily... use a locking pliers and a drilled 1/4" or so shim with a 6-32 screw (a temporary pin setup..) fitting the guide eyelet to get an approximate parallel distance to the side of the lower receiver so that the spring group is slightly loose, not deflecting the hammer-striker unit. Clamp it approximately so the spring lies at about a 40 degree angle similar to Figure 18. Snug the "T" pivot bolt so that the "T" assembly moves easily, but isn't overly sloppy.

Whenever testing anything movable on the receiver, wear safety glasses and be careful; remember, under spring pressure if a clamp comes loose small parts could fly and cause an eye injury!

To determine the motion required for the bolt to move to reliably fire a cartridge, **place some already fired .22 casings into the bar magazine with the rim unblemished where the pin will strike**... you need to see if the firing pin will indent them enough to fire a real cartridge.

Mount the bar magazine in the receiver, and push it down to engage in the first detent. Now push the hammer to the rear watching that the "T" rotates the positioner and advances the first already fired cartridge to the barrel opening.

Hold the gun steady, and release the hammer-striker allowing it to strike the firing pin unit.

The two Small Parts Inc. CSX-0185-05 (or a mix) will likely offer plenty of impact. Or two CSMW-0135-05 units. If you want to try a bit more impact force, try rotating the hammer a bit further before releasing. In this location you cannot add a spacer, since the spring must initiate from a non stressed position to allow for clearance of the firing pin. Experiment until the dent appears equivalent to those already in the fired casings.

The first criterion is moving the positioner an amount to reliably ratchet the Bar Magazine and move back to reset for the next. You must then use that equivalent hammer arc with a correct spring setup to achieve adequate hammer force for firing of the round.

There are many options available to equalize movement required to advance the magazine one round... and hammer-spring movement required for firing a cartridge; the movement required to fire a cartridge must be slightly past the point where the magazine locks to the barrel to insure correct alignment. The arm lengths form the ratio between the hammer-movement and the positioner movement. The amount a compression spring compresses determines the force it exerts. So mounting it on a smaller radius of arc can reduce its effect. You will probably need about 1 1/2" to 2" of arc for hammer movement to fire a cartridge and operate the positioner with a 2 1/2" inch hammer arm and a 7/8" upper right "T" arm.

This means you should have about 3 to 4 inches of total hammer spring; (to allow the compression and still have some remaining gap between the spring coils...) this can be a series of springs of different or similar strengths. Separate them with washers. There could even be an inner and outer spring in the mix, using two different diameters.

You can mount different springs, etc. to modify force, for example,
   · to lessen hammer force you can have the springs operate at a higher point on the hammer arm (lesser radius) or use a lighter spring in the setup series of springs.
   · To strengthen force use a stronger series of springs, or insert an inner spring inside one or more of the outer springs.

It sounds complicated but turns out to not be so difficult. I found smaller springs would work fine, and would serve better for the later Double Action Mechanism. Your trigger pull there must be enough to pull the hammer back and fire a cartridge! So a weaker spring setup will save you finger strain.

Advance to another round and repeat for a couple more times, then advance the magazine bar out of the weapon and examine the rims to see if the firing pin dented them adequately compared to the existing dents in the fired cartridge. This gives you the point where the trigger release should be mounted. Mark the receiver at the location that the hammer must be released from to achieve this impact.

Drill a 9/64" hole in the left receiver plate at the location for the hammer spring guide eyelet and mount the Hammer guide pin, a 3/4 inch long 6-32 screw. You can use perhaps washers, a nylon tubular standoff and a 6-32 nut to set a height to give a correct "centering" between the two receiver panels to parallel match to the hammer spring centering so the hammer spring guide slips easily past one surface of the lower "T" arm, add another spacer above to give the correct spacing to the right receiver plate.

If all seems good, it is time to do the trigger and hammer release setup.

A note on pins and pivots:

- You can sometimes use a screw, and lockwasher with nut or a stopnut. Or you can thread a part with a Tap.
- Sometimes if the item is enclosed between two surfaces like the receiver panels, a cutoff nail will do nicely.
- A Cotter Pin can be used or a thicker nail can be cut off and split at the end with the Dremel Tool so the tabs can be bent to contain parts locked on the pin in a panel or metal fabrication.
- A 16 penny nail can be welded vertically onto metal parts to form a very nice pivot pin. This is tricky welding but I did it in a few spots, and I am not an expert welder.

Some thought must go into the best method to use for your application.

Chapter 8

The Trigger and
Release Pin

In my setup, I used a hammer release mounted radially to the "T" arm pivot. The Hammer release is shown in Figure 23.

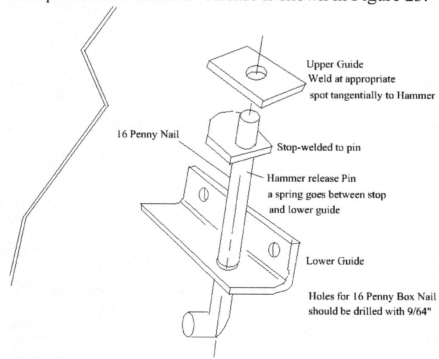

Upper Guide
Weld at appropriate
spot tangentially to Hammer

16 Penny Nail

Stop-welded to pin

Hammer release Pin
a spring goes between stop
and lower guide

Lower Guide

Holes for 16 Penny Box Nail
should be drilled with 9/64"

Fig. 23. Hammer Release

The Hammer Trigger Release pin is made from a 16 Penny Box Nail. Weld a small 14 ga. steel stop near one end leaving about 1/4" of the nail exposed at that one end, and over 1" at the other.

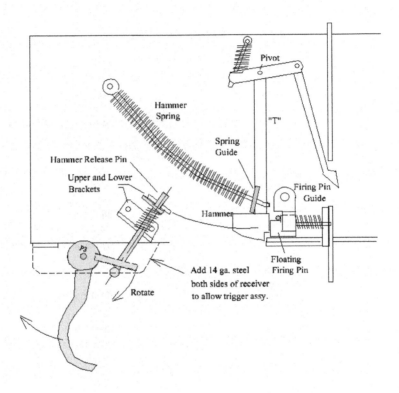

Fig. 24. Trigger/Release Assembly

Make two 14 ga. guides similar to the drawing, they must be no higher than the height of your Bar Magazine guides. Pick a small, stiff spring about 3/4" long from the Ace # 5213517 hardware assortment that will fit nicely over the nail, and mount the parts as shown in Figure 24. The position where bolt operation seemed adequate previously for firing a round is where the release pin should be mounted to operate from the trigger.

Fig. 25. Trigger Release

This required an assembly for trigger mounting slightly below the existing receiver panels, so be sure to weld those on when establishing the trigger mounting. They are shown in Figure 24. You can estimate their size as you examine the positioning for your trigger to release the hammer.

In operating the hammer you must make sure if there is a washer between the hammer drive springs that it does not drag against the receiver sides; also it and the spring must not catch against the hammer release pin.

65

<u>Hint:</u> Remember in the last chapter, one thing that could limit sloppy side movement of the spring would be to twist the spring guide near the upper fastening eyelet so the wide part of the guide is crosswise between the two receiver sides, thus limiting side play of the spring. This means a slight modification of the guide on the lower arm of the "T" assembly. But now the springs cannot bulge significantly to the side as they compress, meaning less possibilities of friction against the receiver sides! Use a fine 400 grit sandpaper to smooth your guide on corners and the edge for a smooth sliding feel.

Grip the washer in Vise-Grip Pliers and grind to reduce its diameter if too large. Possibly some slight drag might occur between the washer and sides if the weapon is on its side, but it should be very light. It is a good idea to bend a slight arc into the entire portion of the spring guide to allow for easy sliding through the spring guide bracket. This arc should be somewhat as the arc around the "T" pivot.

At this point we need to make a trigger too. See Figure 26 for a general idea.

Using the Angle Grinder and Hacksaw, you must cut a rough shape from 1/4" Steel material, be very careful, use the face shield, mask and ear protection. Use the Bench Grinder to get it closer, then a Round File and Dremel type tool.

The trigger will initially serve as a single action trigger to release the cocked hammer, only the front arm area will be needed to release the hammer-striker after it is manually cocked. Later, the intent is to expand the mechanism to a double action, then the rear trigger arm section will be used.

You can add a 14 ga. front metal piece to the trigger unit tab to grab the hammer release if the stub isn't quite enough. It should be shaped like a slight "U" to grab the lower end of the hammer release pin, at the L bend. You can determine the best angle and length of the release pin to set the operation point for the trigger. Drill clearance for a 6-32 screw for mounting the trigger at an appropriate point.

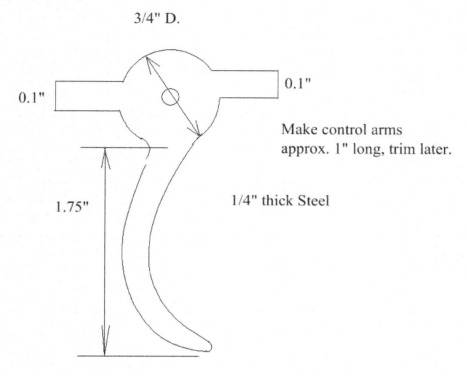

Fig. 26. Basic Trigger

At this point, if you assemble the receivers you should be able to cock the weapon as the bar magazine simultaneously advances, and pulling the trigger should pull the release pin and allow the hammer to drop. **Be sure to have the bar magazine in and an empty cartridge in line, so no damage occurs to the firing pin or stop from hammer impact.**

Thoroughly check operation with a bar magazine and pre-fired casings.

Weld on the one remaining lower attachment support boss that was mentioned in Figure 21 so that it does not interfere with any operating parts. Drill the matching trigger hole through both receiver plates.

See the picture on the next page. Note the trigger stop; it prevents pulling the release so far it leaves the guide hole.

Also note the Hammer and upper "T" bar spring are reversed from my description - this was my first effort. It made me realize it is better to pin spring guides at the fixed end so as not to take up additional space. I subsequently reversed the hammer spring guide.

I had also accidentally cut off the barrel tabs from the receiver pieces during my construction, so you will note the welded barrel supports I added. I had to be careful not to weld any part to the right receiver panel that would not allow it to be removable. Murphy's Law nailed me! When that happens you regroup and go again!

Chapter 9

Attaching the Barrel

The barrel attachment may vary depending on your particular barrel type. So in this case you must adapt to your own barrel. This chapter is only a guide.

My barrel diameter at the chamber end required me to enlarge the point where the barrel lined up and attached to the receiver. I cut the barrel chamber portion off as described in the last chapter and obtained material for a firing pin. This left the barrel with about 20 inches of length.

Use a hand reamer or tapered bit to gently ream the barrel where it will join the receiver. The purpose is to allow an enlarged opening in case of a slight misalignment of the chamber, the coned opening can true up the bullet path as it entered the barrel. A tapered .035 or .040 enlargement should be plenty.

On the receiver pieces, use the Angle Grinder if needed to cut a vertical slot just ahead of the front magazine guide at the barrel opening. Then bend the metal outward on each side to allow enough barrel clearance to allow the barrel to come directly against the front magazine guide at the barrel opening. Use Vise-Grip Pliers to curve the piece near the guide to approximate encircling the barrel somewhat. Most barrels will be about 3/4" diameter at the breech end.

You can weld an attachment to the left side receiver plate to essentially form a circle flange around the barrel. See Figure 28. This will firmly lock the barrel to the front magazine guide once tightened. Keeping a tight fit will keep the detent spring area cleaner as well as ease cleaning of the rifle.

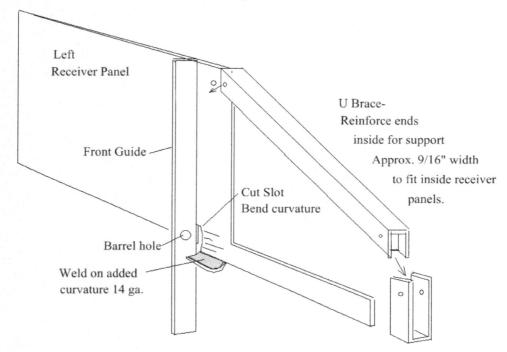

Fig. 28. Barrel Mounting

The idea is to retain two separate receiver pieces, but form a retaining socket for the barrel at the front magazine guide. Run a cleaning rod down the barrel and fasten the receivers together as you socket the barrel to verify the alignment... correct as needed by bending the socket area.

With the barrel in place, and both receiver pieces temporarily attached, measure at the bottom of the extended barrel tabs to get a width for a bottom strip that will mount along the left receiver tab and be welded to the front magazine guide. This piece will

71

provide some lateral and bottom support for the barrel, but will still allow the right receiver to be removable. It forms a "bottom" for the barrel tabs. The barrel will lie in this "trough".

Once you have cut the bottom piece you can remove the barrel and weld this lower piece to the front magazine guide and the lower edge of the **left barrel tab**. Bend as necessary to weld onto the front magazine guide and along the bottom edge of the left tab. Tack first and check barrel positioning then add sufficient weld for completion. Do not weld to the right receiver panel.

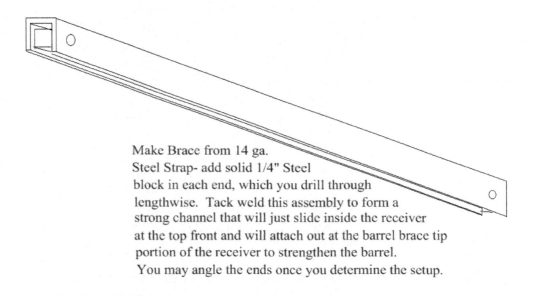

Make Brace from 14 ga.
Steel Strap- add solid 1/4" Steel
block in each end, which you drill through
lengthwise. Tack weld this assembly to form a
strong channel that will just slide inside the receiver
at the top front and will attach out at the barrel brace tip
portion of the receiver to strengthen the barrel.
You may angle the ends once you determine the setup.

Fig. 29. Triangle Brace Detail

Out at the ends of the front barrel support tabs, you will also mount a surrounding bracket loop, which will fasten via a "U" shaped channel triangle to the top of the receiver to add support and solidify the barrel mount. The bracket loop can be welded to the left receiver barrel tab. See Figures 28, 29 and 30. Do not weld to the right receiver.

The triangle support will greatly strengthen the barrel mounting. Cut three strips of 14 ga. steel to form the three sides of the brace, carefully grind the width before welding the assembly so the brace will fit perfectly between the receiver plates with the same width as the magazine guides. Weld supports inside the ends of the channel so that when screws are run through each end to join and support the barrel to receiver, they will be absolutely solid.

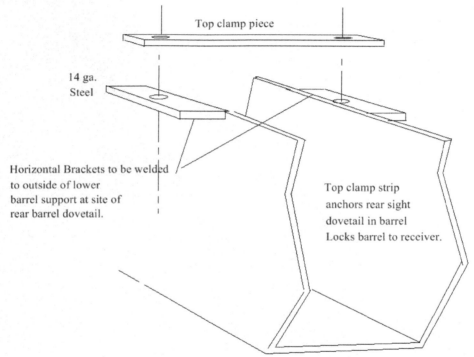

Top clamp piece

14 ga. Steel

Horizontal Brackets to be welded to outside of lower barrel support at site of rear barrel dovetail.

Top clamp strip anchors rear sight dovetail in barrel Locks barrel to receiver.

Fig. 30. Dovetail Clamp

Weld two tabs onto the barrel tabs out front for a dovetail clamp to lock the barrel at the rear sight dovetail; this will lock it against sliding out or rotating, The top crosspiece must fit inside

73

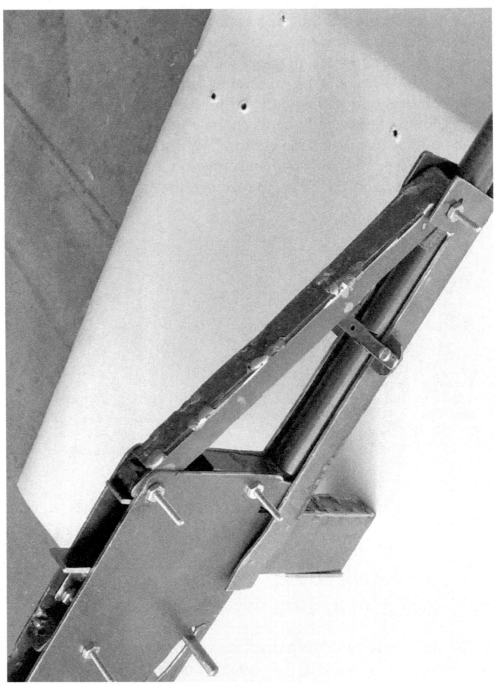

Fig. 31. Barrel Brace and Clamp

and lock the barrel at its rear dovetail; screws will eventually also fasten a Fore-grip on the weapon. You can thread the tabs 6-32 and have separate tabs for the foregrip mounting if you wish.

You should next attach 14 ga. side plates to the lower side area between the front and rear magazine guides. Weld only to the front magazine guide and left receiver panel, so you can still split the receiver and remove the rear magazine guide in case you ever need to modify its slot or the firing pin area. You can make a screw bracket at the rear guide to provide a solid fastening yet allow removal.

Grind or file carefully to do a nice fit and check that the bar magazine still moves smoothly through the weapon as you operate the cocking lever.

You now can loosely fasten the two receiver sides together with all internal parts, then push the barrel into place, and start adding all screws to make the entire barrel and receiver a unit. The barrel breech should be right against the front magazine guide, nice and tight.

Once assembled you need to lay the weapon on its side so the left side of the receiver is facing upward. You will want to make and grind a long accurate matching 12 ga. stiffener rib, about 7/16" to 1/2" wide, then remove the barrel temporarily cover the receiver to protect the sides, and tack weld it perpendicular down the left side of the receiver and extending to the barrel clamp out at the point the angle brace attaches. This is to further stiffen the lateral barrel to receiver attachment.

You will note the photo shows a welded attachment on both sides of my construction... that is because I goofed and cut both barrel supports off during construction of the receivers- and then essentially added them again. It made for a lot more work that would have been unnecessary had I left them on.

(With the additional pieces I added, I did not put a rib on my left panel.)

Push the barrel into the socket on the receiver, and lock the dovetail clamp in place. Tighten receiver screws but check that the trigger and hammer-release movement operates freely.

You can now test the Single Action mechanism.

Chapter 10

Testing

Prior to an actual firing test, be sure to do the previous testing om Chapter 8 on some already fired casings to see if the firing pin indents the fired cartridges similar to those already present.

If you have done that and all other operation seems correct, first try operation with homemade blanks. **Take an unfired .22 cartridge, and grip the bullet in a pliers, hold the case with your thumb and first finger and gently bend the bullet slug to the side almost 90 degrees and then back, it will then come off . Dump the powder into a waste sack.** Make a few of these to use in testing prior to a live-fire. Be sure to dump the powder into your dumpster. You don't want a spark to ignite the unused gunpowder.

Place a "blank" into each chamber of your bar magazine, then insert into the rifle; push the magazine down until it locks into the first detent. Point your rifle in a safe direction and manually operate your hammer to get to the first desired test blank, let the hammer lock back and then pull the trigger to see if the cartridge fires, it will smoke, maybe emit a very small popping noise. If it does, operate the rifle in normal mode to see if each blank goes off. You should get smoke on each blank, showing correct operation. If not, you must check the firing pin alignment and strike, and spring-hammer operation, find what is causing the problem.

But if the rifle basically functions, it is time for the real test--actual rounds.

Build a test jig similar to Figure 32 from scrap wood material. Using measurements from your rifle mechanism, mount the wood front barrel guide and rear support on a base piece. (If you have the stock already mounted, you can add a support on the test jig behind the magazine block to hold it upright.)

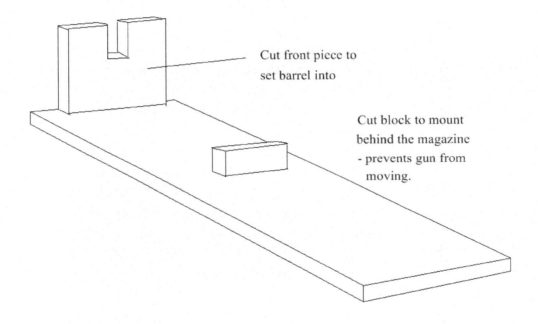

Cut front piece to set barrel into

Cut block to mount behind the magazine - prevents gun from moving.

Fig. 32. Test Jig Setup

The idea here is to go out to a safe shooting area, and set the board jig down, put your rifle mechanism into it, and mount a firing string to the trigger. Then you can load and cock the weapon and go back forty or fifty feet and fire it from a distance. Repeat for all rounds, then you can inspect the bar magazine for any noticeable cracks or deformation. If everything appears good, you can reload and repeat.

I would suggest firing at least 100 or 200 rounds through the rifle, inspecting and checking after each ten rounds before you ever attempt to hold it in your hands to fire.

I am not a Mechanical Engineer, each of us assumes our own responsibility on this; too much depends on an individual ability to do this construction correctly. As for the bar magazine, you can have a gunsmith verify it will safely handle .22 cartridges.

If you are happy with a Repeater, Single Action only rifle, you are there except for adding the stock, a trigger guard, a sight and safety. See Chapters 12 and 13.

You will also want to shorten through bolts on the receiver and barrel attachments and replace any regular nuts with stop nuts that lock in place once you adjust them. Shooting the rifle can loosen standard machine screws and nuts. You may put a thread locking material on threads you expect to be permanent, like sights, that sort of thing.

Chapter 11

Conversion to
Double Action

Look at Figure 33. This is a simplified representation of my double action mechanism.

This drawing actually shows a DAO mechanism, *Double Action Only*, it cannot be cocked; it can only be fired with a full trigger pull action. This is its simplest form, however a latching catch as in the repeater can be added later to allow both single and double action if desired.

This firearm is far more difficult to make compared to the repeater, (the Single Action) previously described in Chapters 7 and 8. Spring tensions are critical because as you pull the trigger, you must overcome those spring forces, specifically the cocking spring and the trigger return spring. Every possible friction point, every spring guide that rubs against a spring, a bad angle during a portion of movement; all of these are working against us. Clearances are critical as well, finding space for the additional mechanism, etc. In some cases you will add washers or somehow create an artificial effect to get the result you want.

Trial and error came into play, I certainly gained a huge respect for the genius of John M. Browning, the inventor of most successful semiautomatic firearms in use today. His designs are totally reliable.

I found at times this firearm was not, though I mostly dis-
covered the weak points and trade-offs and gained a good deal of
knowledge in solving the problems, and probably will continue
to see better setups after this book is finished and printed -as will
you perhaps!

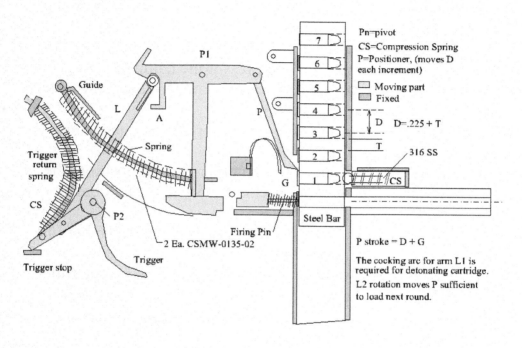

Fig. 33. Double Action Assembly

One point I noticed was that the hammer-striker block that
strikes the firing pin should be large compared to the firing pin
block, weight-wise. Make the firing pin block and pin assembly
smaller if possible. Keep in mind that a larger mass striking a
smaller mass (the firing pin assembly...) imparts a good velocity
to the small mass.   Make sure that even with the stops for the
hammer and firing pin, the hammer will physically push the fir-

81

ing pin into the magazine area enough to dent a cartridge.

In looking at Figure 33, note it requires some additional shaping of the upper "T" bar, and a new link piece. The upper end of the link from the trigger to the "T" bar has a roller head for minimal friction.

Operation is as follows:

- From the position shown, the shooter begins pulling the trigger.
- The hammer starts rotating clockwise around P1 and as it begins rotating left, it compresses the hammer spring.
- The trigger return spring rotates counter-clockwise as the trigger is rotated around P2.
- Positioner, P, meanwhile is pushing the bar magazine downward.
- At the point of almost full hammer cocked position, the bar magazine chamber is engaged by the detent ball above the barrel.
- This grabs and locks the barrel to the firing chamber just below the detent position.
- Slight trigger rotation beyond this point causes the roller link L to hit the small pin A on the "T" assembly which pops the upper link roller out of the circular notch in the "T" bar.
- The upper end of the link rolls left instantly, releasing the "T" bar and hammer-Striker, which allows the hammer to strike the firing pin assembly.
- The firing pin fires the cartridge as the hammer slightly goes past its rest position.
- The hammer returning to the rest position returns positioner, P, to a point just above the next cartridge to be chambered.
- The trigger return spring is curved, and rotates CCW eventually contacting a leverage pad which helps the trigger return spring to retract when the trigger is released. This

also forces the roller link back to position at the hammer notch for the next sequence. See Figure 34.

This constitutes each double action firing sequence. It is similar to a semiautomatic action basically, except DAO requires more trigger pull.

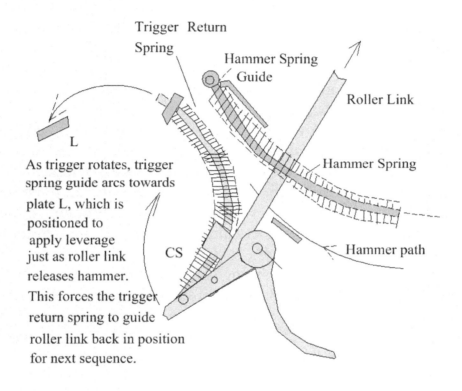

Trigger Return Spring

Hammer Spring Guide

Roller Link

L

As trigger rotates, trigger spring guide arcs towards plate L, which is positioned to apply leverage just as roller link releases hammer. This forces the trigger return spring to guide roller link back in position for next sequence.

Hammer Spring

CS

Hammer path

Fig. 34. Trigger and Roller Link Return

Because trigger action must operate the hammer against the strong hammer spring, as well as position the next round, it is a good idea to minimize the spring as much as possible. I found it was workable to use two CSMW-0135-02 springs to achieve this purpose; in fact after some reduction of friction and binds, I was able to use a single CSMW-0135 spring and a CSMW-0160 spring. The CSMW-0160 is a .032 wire spring and allows a nice light trigger pull! I used a spacer setup (washers) on the spring guide and a washer between the individual components. Another possibility was the CSX-0155-05 springs, or perhaps CSMW-0160-02.

Any spring that is close to 1.5 to 2 inches long and of .035 to .038 wire I believe should be pretty good, and hopefully could be combined with a bit lighter spring like the CSMW-0160 to do the job.

An engineering principle comes into play next involving the movement of trigger required to move the hammer the necessary amount to fire a round. If the trigger moves half as far as the hammer movement required, it takes twice the force of the hammer spring at full cock to pull the trigger, plus a bit for advancing the bar magazine. This gives you an idea... if we can lessen the hammer spring force required, that will be a significant improvement in less trigger pull. Yet we must insure a minimum hammer movement to shift the chambers into alignment and lock, prior to release when the hammer falls.

How do you determine a spring setup that still provides adequate force to fire a cartridge? Operate the mechanism with a bar magazine with already fired shells, turn them to orient a clean rim area to where the firing pin should strike. Check that the firing pin marks appear adequate. That should give you a good estimate.

New "T" Assembly and
Picking Springs

You will make a different "T" assembly from what you used in the repeater, to allow the left upper arm roll off area. I realized at this point there were too many changes to try and modify the repeater "T" assembly. The full trigger motion must be a bit more than needed to actuate each ratchet of the bar magazine, then shortly after it must release the hammer with enough force to fire a cartridge.

The first criterion is moving the positioner an amount to reliably ratchet the Bar Magazine and move back to reset for the next. You must then use that equivalent hammer arc with a correct spring setup to achieve adequate hammer force for firing of the round.

There are many options available to set movement required to advance the magazine one round... and hammer-spring movement required for firing a cartridge; the hammer movement <u>must occur a bit after positioning the round.</u> You will need about 2" of arc for hammer movement to fire a cartridge and operate the positioner with a 2 1/2" inch hammer arm and a 7/8" upper right "T" arm. This means you should have about 3 to 4 inches of total hammer spring; (to allow the compression and still have some remaining gap between the spring coils...) this can be a series of springs of different or similar strengths.

I found two CSMW-0135-02 springs would work in my setup, these are 0.035 diameter wire. Eventually after finding several minor binds or frictions, I was able to use one CSMW-0160 with a CSMW-0135; the 0160 is a lighter spring of .032 wire!   But I expect it may not fire as reliably as the 0135 spring setup.

Also each individual setup is different, a combination of surface smoothness, surface condition, a bind in a spring guide -every conceivable circumstance can affect the friction of parts. So you must experiment here. Try the smaller wire springs first with your setup, then mix a smaller with heavier before going to heavier.

I also can imagine as springs weaken or wear, or some other effect on friction occurs you may at some point need to modify your setup. Perhaps a Teflon spray paint could be used to advantage... you get the idea. There will be some trial and error involved to find a suitable combination.

In measuring during the rifle construction, I found approximately a 60 degree movement of the trigger was about maximum. The "T" assembly and hammer must rotate approximately 40 to 45 degrees based on the springs I used, so this is a fairly good basis for setting up the left "T" bar measurements.

The hammer must not rub on the receiver sides, it must float between to lessen friction.

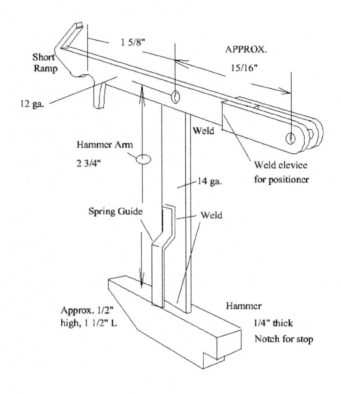

Fig. 35. DAO Hammer

So you must add washers on each side of the "T" pivot pin to help hold the assembly in the center between the left and right receiver. I even welded a washer to each side. It ended up taking one more on each side.

The same thing applies to the hammer spring. This is a case

where a twist in the spring guide making the wide portion perpendicular to the receiver sides could lessen side play and minimize rubbing against the sides.

The radius for the finger portion of the trigger from its pivot was about 1 1/8". The radius to the link arm on the trigger was about 1". This gives a very slight mechanical advantage to the trigger itself.

The arc that the link arm makes must move the left "T" arm sufficiently to make the hammer move the 40 to 45 degrees required. The hammer "T" assembly for the Double Action is as shown in Figure 35. The notch should be very shallow, ground into a nice partial semicircle to accept the roller. (This approximation is for a fairly direct link to "T" action without too much angular component-- mostly perpendicular to the "T" arm...)

The short ramp is to allow the roller on the link to easily roll off at the hammer release point. The metal stub on the bottom just to the right of the partial semicircular notch is to stop the link roller when it re-enters the hammer in preparation for the next firing sequence. It also assists in forcing the roller off the ramp at the hammer release point. You can fine-tune this during testing of the mechanism. You can grind the ramp to adjust the release, as well as modify the stub which applies a push against the link at the release point.

The short angle piece on top of the hammer "T" is to deflect the roller link without snagging.

New Trigger Unit

The trigger unit for the Double Action should be a but fancier than that for the Single Action it turns out ... it uses a clevis design at the rear portion to operate both a special curved trigger return spring, and the roller link described later on. The curved trigger return spring also helps guide the roller link into proper position for each succeeding shot as the hammer returns. See

Figure 36. This shows a general idea of construction. Tack weld the assembly and file to shape a comfortable trigger.
There are two holes at the rear of the clevis: the one nearer the tip is for the trigger return spring; the other is for the roller link.

Ideally, the initial trigger position should be a slight stretch, with a comfortable range as the trigger pull become hardest close to the hammer release. A considerable effort should be spent determining your personal most comfortable position for this.

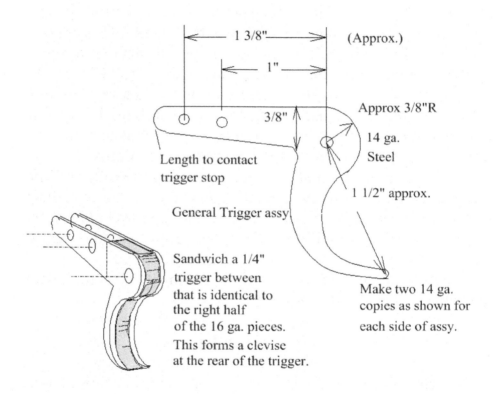

Fig. 36. Trigger for DAO

Roller Link

The Roller Link is shown in Figure 37. The link from the trigger to the "T" will be 14 ga. steel and will run on the outside of the hammer spring flat against the left receiver except where it will pin to the rear trigger arm, and the upper end will utilize the roller for an initial pushing action, until it reaches a full hammer cock position, when the hammer arm tab forces the roller to the left; the roller will suddenly roll aside and release the hammer.

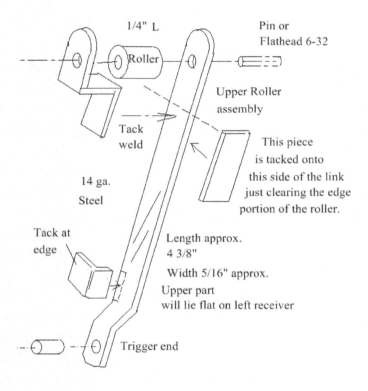

Fig. 37. DAO Roller Link.

The lower pin is made from a 16 penny nail, which fits into the drilled hole in the trigger assembly. The upper roller should be a 1/4" diameter cylindrical brass or steel spacer or standoff, about 1/4" long typically available from an electronics supply house or over the Internet. The one side of the roller bracket can be threaded to lock a 6-32 Flathead Screw. Or you could weld a 16 penny nail in as the axle and grind it flat. Many different ways to achieve the same result. The flat just below the roller and at the right will slide on the "T" as the roller link returns to its ready position for the next round.

The small angle tab at the bottom of the link is a surface that the trigger return spring will rest against at the initial position of the link. It helps return the roller link to the starting position in the "T" slot.

See Figure 38. This figure shows the additional small parts that make up the trigger setup; a return spring guide, the bracket, and a trigger stop that is welded onto the handgrip support at the bottom of the left receiver panel. It is not always possible to show exact placement for your particular setup, but as you build your rifle and see the geometry, you will develop an instinctive feel for placing the parts, and also can place them or even temporarily clamp them in place to check.

The trigger stop can be welded onto the handgrip stub once you determine its location at the spot where the roller link can just re-engage with the "T" assembly. Since the hammer "T" assembly pivots in the exact spot of the Single Action, you can mount it and set up for the roller link and trigger locations.

I added the new upper tang on the hammer spring guide to make sure the roller link would not somehow snag on the hammer spring, however the trigger forcing setup was so positive, the roller link did not even approach the hammer spring.... so it was not needed.

You must test and grind the hammer ramp to allow the roller to release a bit after the magazine chamber has locked. The ramp will end up fairly short with the small tang up top.

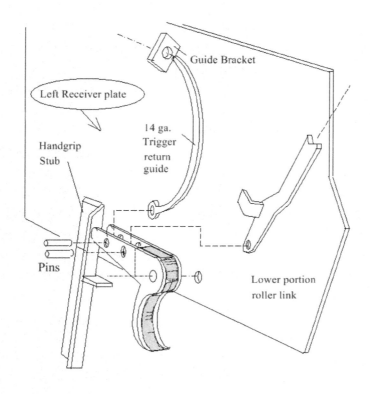

Fig. 38. Setup of Trigger

Now look at Figure 39 on the following page. This photo shows the actual parts layout for the Double Action mechanism. Most of the parts have been discussed and you can see the general layout here. Note the curved trigger spring and guide setup. This arrangement curves to the left as the trigger is pulled simultaneously as the roller link moves upward forcing the hammer to cock. As the link moves it loses contact with the guide at the lower edge of the roller link. (Point "X"....). The roller link eventually releases the hammer which moves to strike the firing pin.

As the trigger is released to return towards its rest position, the link begins moving downward; but because the levering ramp "L" bumper at the left is applying a slight recovery force to the curved trigger return spring the action happens quickly; the guide impinges on the lower link bumper at "X" forcing the roller link to jump down and to the right very rapidly, back to the rest position ready to actuate the hammer again.

Experiment with the curvature of the trigger return spring and the placement of its guide bracket without any hammer or return springs in place until you are sure motion is correct to return the roller link into position for the next action, then add springs to verify. Use some small weak springs from the ACE hardware assortment as the trigger return spring. There are several light brass colored springs, about 3/16"D x 3/4"L, about four in series should work.

Without the hammer spring in place if the roller link binds when extended up all the way and a bit left of the "T" assembly with the trigger pulled, check for interference of the trigger return spring guide and roller link at the trigger clevis. You may need to grind a dogleg into the interference point of the roller link to give space. Some careful inspection is needed here to fix any problem.

Then with the trigger pulled, trigger springs in place, and the roller link at its highest point to the left of the "T" assembly see if the curved trigger spring guide wants to bind a bit or lock up because of its compression, and "locked elbow" position. At this point, if a small 14 ga. leverage bumper plate is added below the left end of the trigger spring guide, to apply a very slight pressure to the bottom of the guide tip at full extension of the guide, it will relieve the bind and will cause the trigger to positively return and reset the roller link at the same time.

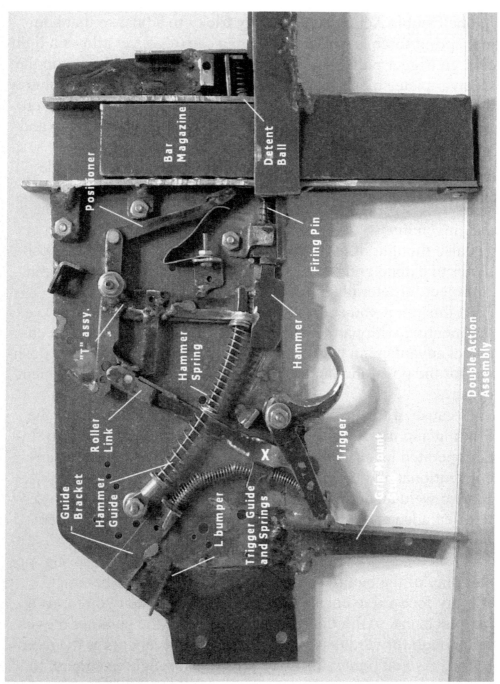

Fig. 39. DAO mechanism

The Double Action setup is very tricky to adjust so that hammer spring force is sufficient to fire a cartridge, yet allows a light enough trigger pull. That is why friction and any rubbing on the receiver plates by springs or the "T" assembly must be absolutely minimal. Some experimentation here should finalize the action and give reliable results. Look at Figure 40 to see the setup and parts that were used.

In the parts shown in Figure 40, you will see a spacer made from a fired .22 shell, of course anything would work, even a small 1/4" steel block with a hole in it. Use your imagination and ingenuity.

I also thought of extending the strap spring used for the positioner to extend and serve as the return spring for the firing pin. A project for later playing!

At this point you are probably confident in your mind as to experimenting with parts placement etc. In general, try for mechanical advantage in trigger pull, and in an efficient angle of pushing for the positioner and roller link, in any aspect of movement of parts.

Because of the limitation in possible trigger motion, it is the limiting and more difficult factor... I thought of using a two finger operated lever for the trigger, but that would look very unconventional and might be unacceptable to some shooters.

Also weld an additional upper and lower spacing boss to set the clearance at the rear of the receiver to allow smooth operation.

A note on operation. Depending on initial hammer spring positioning of the hammer, you may need to push the hammer slightly forward to engage the first cartridge when you insert a bar magazine. After that, as the rounds fire, the hammer moves far enough forward that the positioner positively grabs the next round. As you tighten receiver screws, only tighten enough to remove sloppy action, do not allow a bind to develop.

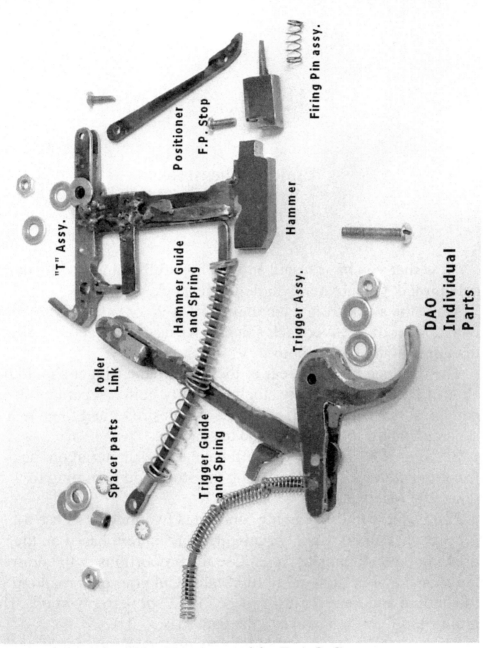

Fig. 40. Parts used in DAO Setup

95

Chapter 12

Building the Stock
and Fore-grip

Now that you have tested and are hopefully happy with your rifle project you are ready to build the stock.

Make the stock from a lamination of 1/2" or 9/16" plywood, with a layer of fir over each side to give a stock of about 1 5/8" thickness at the widest point.

The distance from the rear of the stock to the trigger should be about 13 1/2" or so; on my stock I initially built a separate full handgrip, but your design can be as you desire. I had to go to a separate handgrip and stock due to spacing .

See Figure 41 below. You will have excess material on the front and edges to allow rounding the stock and mounting to your rifle receiver.

Each square in the drawing represents two inches, so use a grocery sack to draw a 2" square grid and pattern based on the drawing on the opposite page. Use the proportions in the drawing to make your drawing to full scale. Cut your pattern along the outline and trace it onto a piece of 1/2" or 9/16 plywood. The grain should run longways to the pattern.

Then use a Jigsaw or Sabre Saw to cut the pattern out of the plywood. Also use a table saw to split a 2x4 to give two side pieces to laminate onto the plywood.

Clamp and glue the side pieces onto the plywood, add additional pieces for the laminated handle; allow to dry.

Your build will likely require a separate stock from the handgrip, as mine did. Make a separate one to fit your grip sized about 4 3/4"L x 1 3/4"W x 1 5/8"D. Laminate and build it out of a scrap of the stock or do it from scratch. Apply glue as with the stock and clamp until dry and solid.

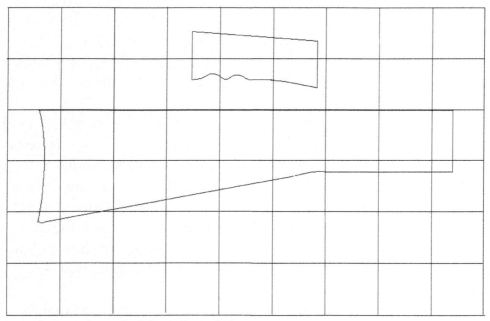

Each Square is two inches

Fig. 41. Stock Pattern

Once dry you can tilt a table saw blade slightly and run the top of the stock through on each side to give a rough bevel like a regular stock. Do a similar rough bevel on the lower side using the tilted blade.

With the separate handgrip, carefully cut roughly to shape, then use a Coping Saw to round the handgrip.

Finish the stock and handle shaping with a belt Sander first with very coarse 80 grit, then with a finer grit and finally with a Palm Sander and hand sanding.

On both the stock and handgrip you must cut slots and a portion out to allow sliding onto the receiver, between the two sides.

Securely weld a narrow "L" stub about 2 1/2" long downward onto the Left Receiver plate; angle it slightly back at whatever angle suits your handgrip style. Then clamp the grip into a vise (protect with scrap on each side) and drill into the handle from the top with a flat spade bit down deep enough to allow sliding the handle up over the stub. You can then drill and tap a hole in the metal stub and drill a matching hole in the handle so that you can fasten it firmly.

You must use care when fitting to your receiver, you will need to cut two slots into the fore end of the stock with a Handsaw or combination of Handsaw and Table Saw. (Caution, no long sleeves to catch, be very careful!) This will allow sliding it into the ½" to 9/16"space between the receiver plates. Once you get it ready you may have to cut off excess material to suit the inner mechanical workings. The distance from the butt of the stock to the trigger should be 13 ½ inches. And your comfort will determine the handle location.

You may need to add metal to the receiver, build it to match your space and mechanism. I had a shorter receiver than described in Chapter 6 in my first prototype, you will note in the photos for the Double Action that I added metal at the rear of each receiver. You must have the space to mount the stock!

Once you achieve the desired fit for the stock, drill through the wood and receiver for three two inch # 10 machine screws, and check the mounting with the screws, washers on each side and nuts.

Next make a foregrip to mount ahead of the receiver. See Figure 42. The length of the foregrip should cover the area in front of the receiver out to the angular brace. Make the brace wide enough to encompass the tabs you mounted for the rear dovetail barrel lock.

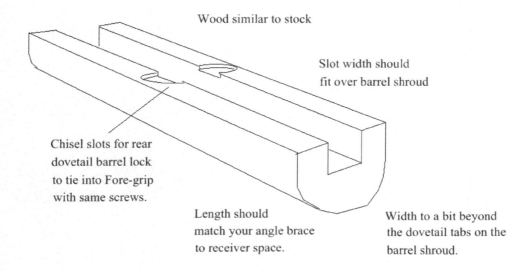

Wood similar to stock

Slot width should
fit over barrel shroud

Chisel slots for rear
dovetail barrel lock
to tie into Fore-grip
with same screws.

Length should
match your angle brace
to receiver space.

Width to a bit beyond
the dovetail tabs on the
barrel shroud.

Fig. 42. Fore-grip

Round the bottom corners and cut a channel in the top so it will fit around the barrel bracing. Use a drill or wood chisel to make recesses for mounting using the existing barrel dovetail fastener.

This unit should allow a natural and smooth, comfortable feel to the front of the rifle and provide a nice finished look.

After you are satisfied with the fit, you can finish the wood surface of the stock and foregrip with a stain and spray varnish or whatever finish you prefer. Cut off the stock mounting screws to a shorter length; you can also check that all receiver screws are a suitable length, use locking nuts after you shorten them. You can also tack weld some of the left receiver screw heads onto the left receiver to lock them in place so they don't fall out each time you take the rifle apart. Be certain any screws you tack are not going to somehow impede removal of the right panel for servicing the rifle.

Figure 43 and 44 show the stock and grip components. Note the cutting and inner details required for sliding over the receiver without interference with internal parts.

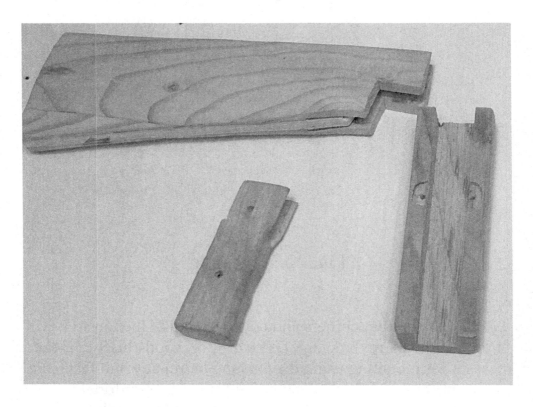

Fig. 43. Stock, Hand-grip and Fore-grip

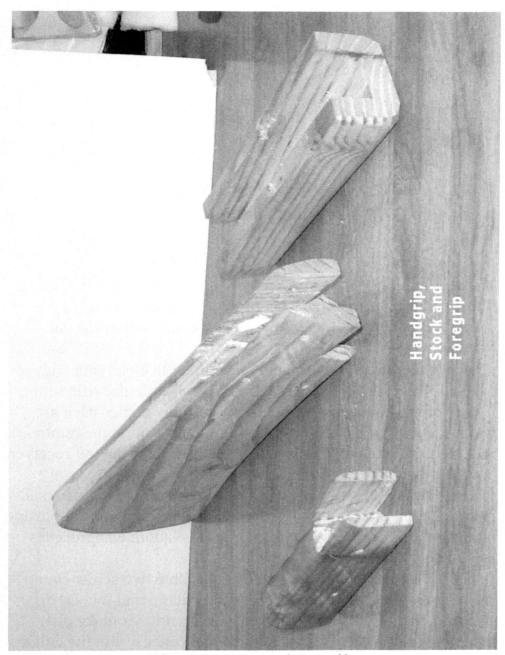

Fig. 44. Internal Details

Chapter 13

A Sight and Safety -
Final Assembly

The remaining items you need are a sight system and a safety.
You also need a finger guard to protect the trigger area.

Your trigger guard is a simple attachment, a strip of 14 ga.
Steel as shown in Figure 45.

Verify the trigger guard height is correct to clear your trigger
during rotation, and set the length for your particular rifle setup,
if your bottom panel on the receiver assembly comes back a
ways, the length can be less. Be sure to not weld to the removable right side receiver, only the lower portion of the left receiver
bottom plate.

The rifle sights can be simple or elaborate, (by that I mean adjustable..) but for the prototype in this book I took the simple approach; this is only a prototype and more elaborate approaches
can be done later.

For the front sight, either buy an adjustable two screw clamp
collar (shaft coupler) from a hardware or industrial jobber, or
Amazon, a collar that will fit over your barrel... or make one,
then you must weld a tall sight bar to the collar or use the collar
to clamp on a tall sight.

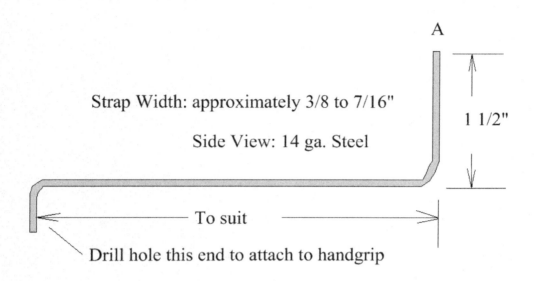

A

Strap Width: approximately 3/8 to 7/16"

Side View: 14 ga. Steel

1 1/2"

To suit

Drill hole this end to attach to handgrip

Fig. 45. Trigger Guard

The rear sight can be a small bar piece welded onto the top of the left receiver, then a V groove is cut in the top center... or drill a centered peep sight hole. With the back sight like this you will adjust the front sight to get on target: If the round hits left, move front sight slightly to left. Opposite if round hits right. Moving the strike point up is done by carefully grinding or cutting the front sight shorter.

The front sight setup is done similar to that shown in Figure 46. The collar is a bit large, 3/4" I.D. And I wished to protect the barrel as this was a single screw lock, not the preferred double type I wanted. So I slid a small strip of wood into the space beneath the screw to protect the barrel... the sight could be mounted further out near the barrel tip for probably better accuracy but I felt there was enough accuracy for say 50 yards to allow the mounting as shown. Also see the rear peep sight in Figure 47 made from a 14 ga. tab which is welded to the left receiver panel.

Fig. 46. Front Gun Sight

The rear sight is welded at approximately the same height from the barrel as the front sight, and both must clear the bar magazine as it protrudes at the top of the receiver prior to the first shot.

Fig. 47. Rear Sight

The picture shows the basic sight attached. If you want this type of simple sight, you should weld a small angle brace part-way up which attaches to the left receiver.

In actuality, the safety can be any device which will block the firing pin. It can be a flat pin, which slides in front of the firing pin block through the receiver panel. I would suggest a 14 ga. piece which slides inside the right receiver face, out it clears the firing pin, when pushed in, it blocks it.

See figure 48. The device slides through the receivers from a side mounted tab. The piece will be slotted, and will be split like a clothespin where it goes through the receiver panel. It will lock reasonably tightly due to the split and the fit of the end.

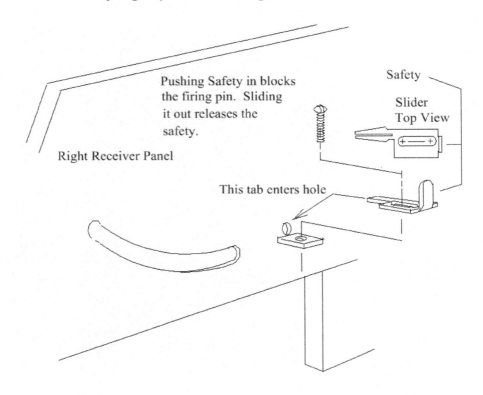

Fig. 48. Safety device

Chapter 14

Some Final
Thoughts

Building the rifle turned out to be quite a project, and I often modified my mechanism a bit; some parts were done trial and error, due to overlooking some small detail, or discovering a space or spring problem.

- The detent ball positioning was my original idea that formed my drive and incentive and the basis for the design; it must be strong enough to lock the bar magazine very securely.

- It worked well, however, I feel a future design should incorporate an additional mechanism with dual chamber insert pins that lock a chamber above and below the detent/barrel position to absolutely align the system; this would be a conditional mechanism that would lock the bar correctly before the trigger could be pulled. It would be analogous to the lock below the cylinder in a revolver, which sets the alignment perfectly in that type of firearm.

- Because the firing pin alignment is so critical for a .22 Long Rifle cartridge, and at the nearest point to the left receiver in this design, I believe if a detent somehow did not grab or was too far off, the firing pin would also miss the round. As I learned to operate the rifle, there was a very distinct feel as each chamber literally "clunked" into position. It is a distinct feel, and once you got used to the rifle it was an unconscious thing to notice without thinking that operation was correct. I grew to expect the clunk, a bit ahead of firing.

- Most problems with firing had to do with a weak firing pin... my goof. Once the firing pin weakness was corrected, many intermittent problems cleared up. Hardening and tempering the pin was the solution. Before I did that, I could fire a few rounds, but then the firing pin would bend and mushroom at the tip, which would start binding in the rear magazine guide. Once hardened and tempered, the pin gave no more problems, and produced a crisp, repeatable indent in each cartridge.

- Often in construction there will be rubbing points or fit details that have to be worked out, a hammer that scrapes, or a sloppy firing pin fit that allows binding. A little bend or redo of alignment; grinding or polishing,, perhaps adding some washers in between a particular pivot should usually give a fix.

- One problem that caused difficulties was side friction of the hammer spring or hammer assembly itself against the receiver sides. This was mostly due to the tight spacing between the sides, about 1/2" to match to the bar magazine.

- I think a clear solution to this problem is to cut and lap weld new rear panel portions to form a wider section of the receiver onto the outside of the original receiver panels close behind the rear magazine; this will give an additional space between the sides to allow for additional clearance.

- Having a stock and a handgrip required a new variation of mounting to the receiver for any adjustment of trigger location. I even had to add to my original receiver with my first construction.

- Sixteen penny nails were handy to make excellent sturdy pivot pins, and with care they could be clamped onto 14 ga. parts and tack welded in place. I used these to advantage for the triggering on the Double Action setup after other methods proved unsatisfactory.

- If the Hammer assembly is made smaller in radius and separate from the "T" positioner, it will have a smaller inertia, less movement and spring requirement, and be less sluggish. The amount of movement required for the hammer would be closer to the trigger motion needed, thus giving more mechanical advantage and trigger pull improvement. A good thing to envision for modification later on. However, it would require a separate linkage setup for the hammer and positioner.

In a homemade firearm like this, ideas for improvements will come as a person fabricates parts and during testing and use. The completion of the project will give many hours of pleasure and initiate building skills along the way. My construction shows a basis for the first try, further improvements are bound to follow!

The main thing is to be safe, there are so many ways to be hurt doing such a project: being cut from metal burrs, burnt from a hot piece of welding, particles of grinding flying into the eyes, causing a fire... the list is endless.

Well, that's about it. Here are the last photos of the final rifle, the long screws have not yet been cut short and lock nuts fitted. I will add a brace on the rear sight. Also the pictures do not show the safety which has not yet been installed.

But this is the end result of that original idea... to use a ball detent lock and a Steel bar magazine... in a homebuilt firearm!

It's your turn. Be responsible, be safe. And have fun along the way!

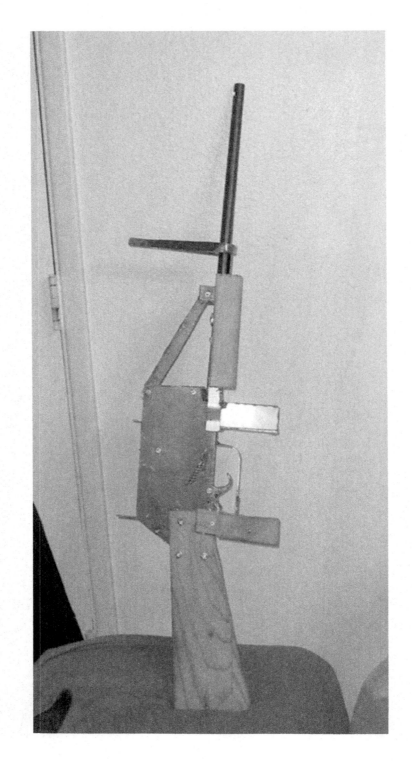

CPSIA information can be obtained at www.ICGtesting.com
Printed in the USA
BVOW04s1107270816

460359BV00005B/41/P